Goethe's Scientific Consciousness

Henri Bortoft

**Institute for Cultural Research
Monograph Series No 22**

The Institute for Cultural Research
P.O. Box 13
Tunbridge Wells
Kent TN3 OJD
England

ICR Monograph Series No 22
ISSN 0306 1906
ISBN 0 904674 10 X

Opinions expressed in Institute for Cultural Research monographs are to
be regarded as those of the authors.

Printed by the Russell Press Ltd
Gamble Street, Nottingham NG7 4ET

Contents

THE AUTHOR

Henri Bortoft graduated from the University of Hull and did postgraduate research in the foundations of quantum physics at Birkbeck College, University of London. He subsequently held a research fellowship in the philosophy of science at the Institute for the Comparative Study of History, Philosophy and the Sciences. He now teaches physics, philosophy and the history of science at Tonbridge School, Kent, England. He has given several courses on Goethe's way of science for audiences in the U.K. and in the United States.

Diagrams drawn by Jackie Bortoft

1. Introduction

Goethe does not fit easily into our categories. He was a man who was both poet and scientist, who is renowned for his poetical and dramatic work and yet who considered that his science was the most important work he had done. We could easily accept a scientist who wrote poetry, perhaps even a poet who wrote about science, but it is difficult to accept a poet who was simultaneously an original scientist, i.e. who did science in an original way. We just cannot easily believe that what he did was really science at all.

When faced with this kind of contradiction in our cultural categories we rationalize. One form which this takes is the accusation of dilettantism. Master among poets Goethe may have been, but as a scientist he was an amateur — and a bungling one at that in his work on colour. We can compare this view with an impression of Goethe's home in Weimar as it was kept towards the end of the last century. Rudolf Magnus described how he found in it numerous specimens from Goethe's work in geology (more than 18,000 specimens), botany and zoology, together with many instruments from experiments in electricity and optics. Magnus was particularly impressed with the wealth of equipment Goethe used in his optical studies, and he said: "I can testify from personal experience to the extraordinary fascination of repeating Goethe's experiments with his own instruments, of realizing the accuracy of his observations, the telling faithfulness with which he described everything he saw."[1] From this description we do not get the impression of a dilettante, nor of a man who thought of himself first and foremost as a poet. In fact Goethe spent twenty years of painstaking work on his research into the phenomena of colour. He said himself: "Not through an extraordinary spiritual gift, not through momentary inspiration, unexpected and unique, but through consistent work did I eventually achieve such satisfactory results." Although Goethe said this specifically about his work on the metamorphosis of plants, it applied equally to all his scientific work.

Another form which the rationalization can take is the apology for the Great Man. We can see this illustrated very clearly in the case of Isaac Newton, to whom Goethe was so opposed in his theory of colour. It used to be an embarrassment that this man, who above all others set the seal on the future development of science in the West, in fact spent more of his time on occult researches and alchemy than ever he did on experimental and mathematical physics. When Newton's alchemical papers were auctioned at Sotherby's in 1936, John Maynard Keynes read through them and declared that Newton was not the first of the age of reason but the last of the magicians. The strategy was then either to ignore this "unfortunate" fact, or else to make apologies for Newton on the basis that great men have their weaknesses and we must not pay too much attention to them. But during the past two decades there has been a significant change in attitude among historians of science. It is now recognised that we cannot just ignore or dismiss approaches which do not fit in with what has become fashionable, if we want to understand how science developed historically. What later generations find an embarrassment, or otherwise objectionable, may in fact be something which needs to be taken seriously. In the case of Goethe, this means taking seriously a radically different way of doing science.

It is a superficial habit of mind to invent the past which fits the present. At the level of the individual, this takes the form of rewriting his own biography. This phenomenon is well-known to psychologists, who recognize it as a variation of the self-fulfilling prophecy. The same mental habit can be seen operating at a more general historical level, where it takes on the form of an assumption that the purpose of the past was to prepare the way for the present. But the past, in this case, becomes no more than an extrapolation from the present. In other words, it is our invention. The result of doing this is that history can be told as a simple tale, because it seems as if there is a single, continuous line leading from the past to the present. The characters in this single-line story fall into two simple categories: forward-looking or backward-looking, depending on whether they seem to fit on the line of extrapolation or not.[2]

Now that this kind of superficial story has been exploded by studies in the history of science, it is clear that there never was a single line of development leading to the kind of science we have today. Furthermore, it has also become clear, from these same studies, that the reasons for the success, or otherwise, or a particular science are not internal to that science. It has been widely believed that science advances by the use of its own internal method for attaining the truth, so that scientific knowledge is legitimated by its own authority. However, it turns out that there is no such method, and science is best understood as a culturally-based activity, i.e. as the product of a social process. Hence, the reasons for the acceptance of a scientific theory often have more to do with complex cultural factors than with the intrinsic merits of the theory in question. This has been borne out, for example, in studies of the seventeenth-century scientific revolution, where it has been shown that the success of the mechanical philosophy was due as much to external political and religious reasons as to it having been shown to be true by any internal scientific method. There are deeply rooted philosophical fashions in science, without which there would not be any science, but which stand outside the orbit of what can be verified scientifically. It is useful to remember this when looking at Goethe's way of science. For example, Goethe's physics of colour contradicted Newton's, and if it is believed that Newton's physics of colour has been shown to be true by "scientific method", then it *must* appear that Goethe's physics was wrong.

It now becomes clearer why Goethe's scientific work has often been received with disbelief. This does not necessarily have anything to do with the intrinsic scientific merit of his work. It has more to do with the state of mind (and what formed it) of those who reject his work as "unscientific" or "wrong". However, it is noticeable that both the rejection and the rationalization of Goethe's scientific work often come from students of the humanities, and not so much from scientists. It is often those who are primarily interested in Goethe as a poet who have the greatest difficulty integrating his scientific work into their perspective. Among scientists we often find respect for Goethe's scientific endeavours, even when there is disagreement. It is acknowledged, for example, that he was a pioneer in the study of plant and animal form — for which he coined the term 'morphology'. There is also some speculation that he anticipated the theory of evolution. This is a notoriously tricky point, and there have been many arguments for and against it. The difficulty is resolved when it is realised that today evolution is identified with Darwin's mechanism of random variation and natural selection. This means that there can be other ideas of evolution which are not recognised as such. For Goethe, as for his contemporaries in the philosophy of nature, there certainly was the idea of evolution. Frau von Stein wrote in a letter in 1784 that "Herder's new writing makes it seem likely that we were plants and animals. Goethe ponders now with abundant ideas over these things, and what has first passed through his mind becomes increasingly interesting."[3] The idea of evolution was certainly in Goethe's mind, but it was not *Darwinian* evolution.

Goethe's major study in physics was concerned with colour. His magnum opus, *Theory of Colours*, was rejected by the establishment because of the attack on Newton which it contained. Newton had been raised on a pedestal by those who came after him, so that Goethe's physics of colour rebounded on its originator because it does not look like physics, as we have come to recognize this science. In fact, on account of this work, Goethe is now looked upon by experimental psychologists of colour as one of the founders of their science. What interests the physicist today about Goethe's work on colour is not so much the details, but the *kind* of scientific theory which he developed. This was very different from the kind of theory which aimed to go behind the phenomenon as it appeared to the senses in order to explain it in terms of some hidden mechanism supposed to be more real. Goethe's approach was to avoid reducing the phenomenon to the mere effect of a mechanism hidden behind the scenes. Instead, he tried to find the unity and wholeness in the phenomena of colour by perceiving the relationships in these phenomena as they are observed. The result was a theory which could be described as a phenomenology of colour, rather than an explanatory model. This will be discussed in more detail below. In thus renouncing models, and rooting the theory in the concrete phenomenon, Goethe now sounds very much in line with the debates about the nature of physical theory which have arisen through the development of quantum physics. His work was in fact discussed in this context at a conference on the quantum theory held in Cambridge in 1968.[4] This comparison may well be superficial, but it does mean that Goethe's scientific method, and the philosophy of science which it reflects, are taken seriously by modern physicists who are faced with an epistemological crisis in their science.

But the value of Goethe's science is not revealed by assimilating him into the mainstream. Unfortunately historians of science are only interested in whether Goethe's work is a contribution to biology, or experimental psychology, or the method of physics. This approach to Goethe misses what is important, and interesting, in his scientific work. The factor which is missing from this academic approach is simply Goethe's whole way of seeing. In a letter from Italy in 1787, Goethe wrote: "After what I have seen of plants and fishes in the region of Naples, in Sicily, I should be sorely tempted, if I were ten years younger, to make a journey to India — not for the purpose of discovering something new, but in order to view in my way what has been discovered."[5] Goethe was indicating here that the discovery of new facts was of secondary importance to him. What mattered was the *way* of seeing, which influenced all the facts. His scientific work was fundamentally an expression of this way of seeing, with the result that it is present throughout all of it, immediately yet intangibly. What we recognize as the content of Goethe's scientific work should really be looked upon as only the container. The real content is the way of seeing. So what we have to aim for, if we are to understand Goethe's scientific consciousness, is inside-out to what we expect, because it is to be found in the way of seeing and not in the factual content of what is seen.

The problem for us is that we think of a way of seeing as something entirely subjective. As victims of the Cartesian confinement of consciousness to the purely subjective, we cannot believe at first that what Goethe experienced as a way of seeing could be an objective feature of the world. The difficulty here comes from the fact that a way of seeing is not itself something which is seen. What is experienced in the way of seeing cannot be grasped like an object, to appear as a content of perception. What is encountered in the way of seeing is the *organization* or *unity* of the world. Just as the organization of a drawing is not part of the sense-perceptible content of the drawing (whereabouts on the page is the organization?), so the organization of the world of nature is not part of the sensory content of that world.[6] But what 'organization' and 'unity' mean turns out to depend on the *mode* of consciousness — this will be discussed in section 2.3 below.

To understand Goethe's way of seeing we would have to experience it for ourselves. We could only really understand it by participation, which means we would each experience Goethe's way of seeing as the way in which our own mind became organized temporarily. This brings us to another problem. If we believe that a way of seeing is only a subjective factor, then we must believe Goethe's way of seeing died with him. If this is so, then any attempt to understand it would entail the absurd requirement of trying to become Goethe! But this problem disappears when it is recognized that what is experienced as a way of seeing *is* the unity of the phenomenon. It follows immediately that any number of individuals can experience the same way of seeing without the restriction of time. A way of seeing has the temporal quality of belonging to 'the present' instead of to the past. It is more like an event of perception in which we can learn to participate, instead of repeating something which once happened and has now gone. Goethe himself had to learn to see in the way which we now call "Goethe's way of seeing". We will now explore this way of seeing, first as it is present in his work on colour, and then in his work on organic nature.

2. Making the Phenomenon Visible

Goethe became interested in colour during his Italian journey (1786-88). When he returned home he reminded himself of Newton's theory about colour, as this was presented in the books available to him, and decided to do the famous experiment with the prism himself. However, having borrowed a prism, his interest and time were then taken up with other things. He did nothing about it, until the time came when he was obliged to give the prism back. It was then too late to repeat Newton's experiments, as he had intended, and so he just took a rapid glance through the prism before handing it back. What he saw astonished him, and the energy of his astonishment was so great that it launched him into a research programme on colour which was to take nearly twenty years. This is what Goethe said about that experience:

"But how astonished was I when the white wall seen through the prism remained white after as before. Only where something dark came against it a more or less decided colour was shown, and at last the window-bars appeared most vividly coloured, while on the light-grey sky outside no trace of colouring was to be seen. It did not need any long consideration for me to recognize that a *boundary or edge is necessary to call forth the colours*, and I immediately said aloud, as though by instinct, that the Newtonian doctrine is false."[7]

What was the Newtonian doctrine, and why did Goethe believe that what he saw — or rather failed to see — indicated so strongly that it was wrong? To answer this question it will be necessary to begin with a brief account of Newton's experiments with a prism.

2.1. Newton's Experiments

Newton's work on colour also began with a surprise. He made a small circular hole in the window shutter of a darkened room, and passed the beam of sunlight which it formed through a glass prism onto the wall. He observed the colours which formed there, but then he noticed that the image of the aperture on the wall was oblong, and not circular as he would have expected it to have been. Other experiments were then made to explore this peculiarity. In one of these experiments he used a second small aperture in a screen, placed after the prism, to select light of one colour only, which he then passed through a second prism. He found that no further colours were formed by the second prism. But he also found that the angle through which the light was deviated by the second prism depended on the colour — violet being deviated the most, and red the least. He called this the *Experimentum Crucis*, and on the basis of what he saw in it he made an inductive leap to propose the cause of the unexpected shape of the image which he had noticed at first.[8]

Newton's theory was that sunlight is not homogeneous, as had been supposed, but "consists of rays differently refrangible". These rays are all refracted through different angles when the sunlight is incident on the prism, and the colours which are experienced correspond with these different angles of refraction. Thus, the rays which are least refracted produce the sensation of red, whereas the sensation of violet is produced by the rays which are refracted most. It is, therefore, the separation of these rays by the prism which produces the oblong coloured image of the circular aperture. Thus was born the well-known theory that colourless light is a mixture of all the colours of the spectrum, which are separated out by a prism. As such it is known to every schoolboy and repeated by every textbook writer. Yet this is not what Newton thought. In his major work on light he said:

"And if at any time I speak of light and rays as coloured or endowed with colours, I would be understood to speak not philosophically and properly, but grossly, and according to such conceptions as vulgar people in seeing all these experiments would be apt to frame. For the rays to speak properly are not coloured. In them there is nothing else than a certain power and disposition to stir up a sensation of this or that colour."[9]

The trouble is that Newton did often speak of sunlight as being composed of rays of differing colours. Goethe pointed out that this could not be so because every coloured light is darker than colourless light, and if colourless light were compounded of coloured lights then brightness would be compounded of darkness, which is impossible. But Newton's view that colour is a sensation in the observer, and not a physical phenomenon, was quickly forgotten by his followers. One result of selecting only a part of Newton's theory is that what is said about it today is often simply nonsense.[10]

Time and again the myth is repeated that Newton showed by experiment how colourless light contains a mixture of colours, which are separated by a prism. It is presented as if this were available to the senses and could be observed directly. Yet there is no experiment in which this separation of the colours can be seen directly with the senses. Newton attempted to prove that this is what is happening by reasoning *based* on experiments. Originally it was an insight for him, and as such it cannot be reached directly by experiment, or by logical reasoning based thereon. Subsequently he tried to present it as a consequence of following a definite method. This was the mathematical method, based on geometry, but with experiments replacing verbal propositions. Newton's presentation must be followed with care, and in the spirit in which it was intended, otherwise the unwary reader can easily fall into the trap of believing that Newton had seen with his eyes what cannot in fact be seen directly at all.

What Newton did do, by his combination of experiments and theory, was to replace the phenomenon of colour with a set of numbers. In so doing, he fulfilled the aim of the programme for the scientific investigation of nature developed by Galileo and others. The introduction of the quantitative, mathematical method into science led inevitably to the distinction between primary and secondary qualities. Primary qualities are those which can be expressed mathematically in a direct way — such as number, magnitude, position, and extension. By contrast, qualities which cannot be expressed mathematically in a direct way — such as colour, taste and sound — are said to be secondary. This distinction was subsequently made into a dualism in which only the primary qualities were considered to be real. A secondary quality was supposed to be the result of the effect on the senses of a primary quality, being no more than a subjective experience and not part of nature. The result of this step was that some of the features of nature which are encountered most immediately in experience were judged to be unreal, just illusions of the senses. One group of qualities, the primary ones, was imagined to be behind the other group, hidden by the appearances, so that a secondary quality was understood when it was explained how it could have arisen from primary qualities alone. In other words, the secondary qualities are really primary qualities which manifest themselves in perception in a manner which is different from what they really are, so that the task of science is to reduce all the phenomena of nature ultimately to such primary qualities as shape, motion and number.

Newton attempted to fulfill this programme in two ways in his work on colour. Firstly, by showing that different colours are refracted through different angles, he was able to replace the colours by a numerical measurement. Thus he could eliminate colour from the scientific description of the world by correlating it with the 'degree of refrangibility' (which we now call 'angle of refraction'). A series of numbers could then be substituted for the sensory experience of different colours. Secondly, Newton tried to imagine a mechanical model for light, whereby the dispersion of colours by the prism was explained in terms of light corpuscles, or globules, which all moved with the same velocity in vacuum but different velocities in glass. Thus, according to this model, Newton considered the speed of the imagined light particles to be the objective basis of our experience of colour — although he also seems to have considered the size to be an important factor on another occasion, with the corpuscles which caused the sensation of red being bigger than those which caused blue. Whatever the particulars of the model, the important point is that the secondary quality of colour is replaced completely by primary qualities which can be represented quantitatively. This strategy of trying to explain a phenomenon by means of a microscopic model — which is based on images borrowed from the sense-perceptible world — became a standard practice in the mainstream of physics up until this century. Newton's own attempt to provide a mechanical model for light was not successful. The model which eventually gained acceptance was the wave model. According to this, light is a wave motion, with different colours corresponding to waves of different frequencies. Once again the phenomenon is reduced to a mathematical magnitude. The model is different, but the result is the same: colour is written out of nature.

2.2. The Primal Phenomenon of Colour

When Goethe saw that the prismatic colours appeared only where there was a boundary, he recognized that the theory of the colours being contained already in the light must be wrong. There must be light *and* dark for the colour phenomenon to arise, not just light alone. He investigated this carefully by constructing simple boundaries from which all secondary, complicating factors were removed. Anyone who has a prism can repeat Goethe's observations. Just make a card with a straight boundary between black and white regions, and look at the boundary through the prism (the edges of which should be parallel to the boundary) with the card in either of these orientations:

(a)   (b)

In both cases vivid colours are seen parallel to the boundary. In orientation (a) the colours appear in the white region just below the black, with red nearest to the boundary, then orange, and yellow furthest away from the boundary. In (b) the colours also appear at first to be in the white region, but careful observation (e.g. by placing the tip of a pencil on the boundary for reference) reveals that they are in fact being seen in the black region just below the white. Again, the colours are parallel to the boundary, but with this orientation of the card the colours are blues, with light blue nearest to the boundary and violet furthest into the black. To begin with it is best to concentrate on the central boundary and ignore the colours at the top and bottom edges of the card.

When observing the phenomenon of colour in Goethe's way it is necessary to be more active in seeing than we are usually. The term 'observation' is in some ways too passive. We tend to think of an observation as just a matter of opening our eyes in front of the phenomenon, as if it were something that happens to us when visual information flows in through the senses and is registered in consciousness. Observing the phenomenon in Goethe's way requires us to *look*, as if the direction of seeing were reversed, going from ourselves towards the phenomenon instead of vice-versa. This is done by putting *attention* into seeing, so that we really do *see* what we are seeing instead of just having a visual impression. It is as if we plunged into seeing. In this way we can begin to *experience* the *quality* of the colours.

But Goethe's encounter with the phenomenon did not stop at this stage of observation. He would then repeat the observations he had made, but this time doing so entirely in his imagination without using the apparatus. He called this discipline *Exakte sinnliche Phantasie*, which can be translated 'exact sensorial imagination'. In this case it would mean trying to visualize making the observations with the prism, and seeing the qualities of the different colours in the right order at a boundary as if we were producing them. This would then be transformed in imagination into an image of the colours with the boundary in the opposite orientation, and then transformed back again. The process can be repeated several times. The aim is to think the phenomenon concretely in imagination, and not to think about it, trying not to leave anything out or to add anything which cannot be observed. Goethe referred to this discipline as "recreating in the wake of ever-creating nature". Combined with active seeing, it has the effect of giving thinking more the quality of perception and sensory observation more the quality of thinking. The purpose is to develop an organ of perception which can deepen our contact with the phenomenon in a way that is impossible by simply having thoughts about it and working over it with the intellectual mind. For example, through working in this way a relationship between the qualities of the colours may be perceived. Black, violet and blue begin to be perceived as belonging together, as if there were a unity in these colours which is not perceived at first. The same can be found with white, yellow, orange and red. Sometimes this relationship in the colours is perceived as having a dynamical quality, even though there is no movement in a physical sense. Thus what is perceived by the senses as simply different colours which are separate, begins to be perceived more holistically. The colours are perceived belonging together in a unity which is present in the phenomenon but not visible like the colours themselves. If there is unity in the colour phenomenon at a boundary, then it is not like something which we may have simply overlooked at first. It is not like a colour which we may have missed — as if we could say "there is red, and there is yellow, and there is the unity over there". It is in fact not visible to the senses (though it may seem to be so), and yet it can be perceived — this point will be taken up in some detail in section 2.3 below.

Although the unity in the colour phenomenon may begin to be intimated by working with the prism in the way described above, it is difficult for it to emerge clearly in these circumstances. This is because the appearance of the colours in this case depends on the peculiar shape of the piece of glass. Goethe believed that this was a complicating factor, and because of this the phenomenon of prismatic colours was not a suitable basis from which to understand the origin of colours. He also believed that there must always be some instance in nature where a phenomenon occurs in the simplest way possible, without any secondary factors to disguise what is essential. He had already recognised from his first observation with the prism that light and dark were necessary "to call forth the colours". So if he could find an instance in nature of the "coming into being" of colours out of light and dark alone, then he would have read the origin of colours directly in nature itself. He called such an instance an *Urphänomen*, which can be translated 'primal phenomenon', and he described it as "an instance worth a thousand, bearing all within itself". He saw the proper task of physics as being to find the primal phenomenon for any particular field of study, and to resist the temptation to try to go beyond it by imagining a hidden mechanism as Newton and others did.

Goethe discovered the primal phenomenon of colour in the colours of the sun and the sky. On a clear day the colour of the sky overhead is a brilliant blue, which becomes lighter in shade as the angle of vision decreases towards the horizon. But if we were to go up a mountain, the colour overhead would progressively darken until it became violet. If we could go higher still it would darken further until it became black. When

15

we look at the sky overhead we are seeing darkness through the atmosphere which is illuminated by the sun. The quality of the blue we see depends on the thickness of the atmosphere through which we are seeing the darkness of outer space. The greater the thickness of the atmosphere, the lighter the shade of blue. Goethe recognised that the role of the atmosphere here is to be a light-filled medium because it is illuminated by the sun. So when we look at the sky we are looking at dark through light, and the effect of this is to lighten the dark progressively into lighter shades of blue as the proportion of the light-filled medium increases. Thus the origin of blue is the lightening of dark which occurs when dark is seen through light. In this way Goethe learned to see the "coming into being" of the various shades of blue in the phenomenon itself.

The origin of red and yellow can be discovered in the changing colour of the sun. When it is overhead on a clear day the sun is yellow, and it darkens in colour towards red as it moves closer to the horizon at sunset. In this case we are looking at light through the atmosphere, and the role of this medium is now to darken what is seen in proportion as its thickness increases. If we were to go higher up, the sun would become whiter as the atmospheric thickness decreased. Thus the origin of yellow, orange and red is the darkening of light which occurs when light is seen through dark. Here also Goethe learned to see the "coming into being" of the colours in the phenomenon itself, so that from this "instance worth a thousand, bearing all within itself" he could understand how they arise out of light and dark exclusively.

Now we can read the colours of the sun and the sky in the prismatic colours, and vice-versa. It is well worthwhile doing this by exact sensorial imagination, instead of just following it in the verbal-intellectual manner. Beginning with the colour of the sky, we can visualize the change in quality of the colour from black through to pale blue as the thickness of the atmosphere increases. Then we can visualize the colours formed with the prism when the boundary is in orientation (b). We can see the same order in the quality of these prismatic colours as in the colours of the sky. The sequence from black to violet to pale blue now corresponds to an increasing thickness of cross-section of the prism which we are looking through. Since we have noticed before that these colours are seen in the black region, we can now recognize that what we are seeing here is different degrees of the lightening of dark. Repeating this exercise in imagination with the colour of the sun, and the prism with the boundary in orientation (a), we can again recognize the same order in the qualities of the colours in the two phenomena. This time we are seeing the darkening of light. The colours deepen from yellow to orange and red as

16

the thickness of the atmosphere, or the cross-section of the prism, increases. The prism plays the same dual role of the medium as the atmosphere does, depending on whether it is light which is seen through dark or vice versa. We may not know in detail yet how it comes about that we are seeing dark through light or light through dark with the prism, and we cannot go further into this here, but what we have done is sufficient to illustrate Goethe's way of learning from the phenomenon itself in such a way that it becomes its own explanation.[11]

Although the practice of thinking the phenomenon concretely by exact sensorial imagination is irksome to the intellectual mind, which is always impatient to rush ahead, its value for developing perception of the phenomenon cannot be overestimated. It has been mentioned already how this discipline can be instrumental in perceiving a phenomenon holistically. The practice of it, as in the case just described, shows how this comes about from the demand which it makes on us to visualize the phenomenon comprehensively. It also shows how the demand to produce the phenomenon for ourselves helps thinking to enter into the coming into being of the phenomenon, instead of analysing what has already become. What Goethe discovered in this way was a dynamical polarity in the colour phenomenon. As well as the unity within the quality of the colours in each orientation of the boundary, which is a real relationship between the colours, there is also a unity between the two different colour phenomena. This is the unity of a polarity, like positive and negative electric charge. Because one and the same boundary can be in two different orientations with respect to the prism, these two colour phenomena are really inseparable. We may think of them separately, and in any particular case we must choose one and not the other because we cannot have both simultaneously at the same boundary. But they are not essentially separate from each other because each one determines the possibility of the other, i.e. if one is possible then the other must be too. So this polarity is essentially holistic and not analytical. We can begin to experience it as such in the colours of the sun and the sky, as well as with the prism, by working intentionally with exact sensorial imagination instead of with the verbal-intellectual mind.

Goethe described this polarity as "the deeds and sufferings of light", a poetic expression which is as precise in the science of quality as any mathematical expression in the science of quantity. But "the deeds and sufferings of light" is already a second degree polarity. The primary polarity is the unity of light and dark. When we think of 'light and dark' with the verbal-intellectual mind we interpret it analytically — we have a mental impression of 'light' and 'dark', each on their own, joined together externally by 'and'. But this misses out the fact that we cannot

17

have the one without the other — it is as if the possibility of each one is determined by the other. There is a wholeness in the boundary itself which we usually do not notice. It is true of all opposites that they mutually determine each other, and hence that there is a unity in their opposition. Aristotle said that the knowledge of opposites is one. The trouble is that it is not one for the verbal-intellectual mind because of its analytical character. The wholeness of polarity can only be perceived when the mind works in a more holistic mode, otherwise it is only an abstraction. The practice of exact sensorial imagination is a door to this mode. This will be discussed further in the section 2.3. below.

It is possible to have both "poles" of the colour phenomenon present simultaneously by making a card with a broad white band on a black background:

If we now imagine the white space shrinking in the vertical direction, so that the two horizontal boundaries come closer together, a point will be reached where the two polar phenomena meet and overlap. We can find out what happens when they do by making a card with a narrow white band on a black background:

Where they meet we see green, for the first time, and there is now something like the "spectrum of light" which Newton described — the pattern of light and dark on this card being the same as for a narrow slit in a screen illuminated from behind.[12] But this has been reached in a very different way from Newton's. By following the coming into being of green in this way, Goethe was able to recognise that the idea of a spectrum of light was an error of judgement, arising from the fact that "a

18

complicated phenomenon should have been taken as a basis, and the simpler explained from the complex". This error of judgement is a consequence of trying to understand the origin of the phenomenon in terms of the finished product. The Afghan poet and philosopher, Jalaluddin Rumi, described this approach in general as trying to "reach the milk by way of the cheese".[13] Following this analogy, the naive interpretation of Newton's theory of the prismatic colours, described above, amounts to the assertion that cheese comes from milk because cheese is already there in milk. The more sophisticated version, which Newton himself advocated, is the equivalent of saying that a disposition towards cheese exists in the milk, but it only becomes the cheese experience when it enters a human digestive system. Goethe's approach, on the other hand, is the equivalent of trying to understand cheese by following through the process by which it is produced.

When the prismatic colours are understood in Goethe's holistic way, the quality of each colour becomes something which is intelligible in itself and not just an accident. In Newton's account of the origin of the colours there is no reason why the colour 'red' has the quality of red, or why 'blue' has the quality of blue, or why the colours are in the order observed and not in some other order. The intelligibility of the colours in themselves disappears in the analytical approach, and what is left seems to be merely contingent. It is no answer to be told that the order the colours appear in is the numerical order of their wavelengths, and that red has the quality of red because its wavelength is seven-tenths of a millionth of a metre, whereas violet has the quality of violet because its wavelength is four-tenths of a millionth of a metre. There is simply no way in which these qualities can be derived from such quantities. But it is very different when the colours are seen comprehensively in Goethe's way. The order of the colours is now necessary instead of contingent, and hence the quality of each particular colour becomes intelligible in itself instead of appearing accidental.

A particularly vivid illustration of the difference between these two approaches to colour is given by making a white card with a narrow dark strip:

When this is looked at through the prism, the order of the colours is seen to be inverted compared with the previous case. Now violet and red overlap, instead of yellow and light blue, and where they meet a ruby-magenta colour appears instead of green. So the order of the colours from the top border downwards is blue, violet, ruby-magenta, red, orange, yellow. This is not mentioned by Newton. But that is not surprising, since it would have to be called the "spectrum of dark", and this would be impossible if the colours were derived from light alone in the way that Newton believed. Yet this is often the first colour phenomenon a person sees with a prism, because it is the one which is formed by the bar across the middle of a window. When people see this who remember what they learnt about the spectrum at school, they are naturally puzzled by what they see. In some cases, in order to reduce the cognitive dissonance of this situation, they assume that what they are seeing must be wrong! Goethe recognized that "the senses do not deceive, but the judgement deceives". In this case it is the judgement of the Newtonian theory which deceives, and it is only when this particular phenomenon is understood in terms of the primal phenomenon of colour that it becomes intelligible.

2.3. Goethe's Scientific Consciousness

It would be easy to present Goethe's work on colour as if it had been done in a purely empirical manner, i.e. as if he had reached his knowledge of the origin of colours through his senses alone. It has been mentioned already that this is not true, even though it may seem to be so at first. The world which we know is not in fact visible to the senses, although this is easily overlooked. We do see the world, of course. But, as the well-known philosopher of science, Norwood Russell Hanson, put it, "there is more to seeing than meets the eye".[14] If we want to understand what scientific knowledge is, we have to learn to recognise the extra, non-sensory, factor which transforms sensory experience into cognitive perception. This means learning to recognise the fundamental incoherence of empiricism as a philosophy of science. This has to be done first, before we can understand the nature of Goethe's scientific consciousness.

2.3.1. Knowing the World

According to the philosophy of empiricism, and to common sense, we know the world through experience. Nobody would doubt that we do. But empiricism, and common sense, both interpret experience to mean *sensory* experience. So what this philosophy asserts is that knowledge of the world comes through the senses — we open our eyes, and other organs of sensory perception, and what is transmitted through these channels into consciousness is knowledge of the world. Now, although we could not see the world without the senses, we also could not see it with the senses alone. Knowledge of the world is based on sensory experience, but it is not the same as sensory experience. There is always a non-sensory factor in cognitive perception, whether it is everyday or scientific cognition. Knowing even the simplest fact goes beyond the purely sensory. Although we do know the world through experience, there is another dimension to this experience, a non-sensory dimension, which is really the dimension of the mind. The difficulty we have in recognising this at first is a consequence of our identifying mind with a disembodied intellectual function, a prejudice that has deep historical roots in Western culture and is institutionalized in the educational system.

The fact that there is literally more to seeing than meets the eye, can be appreciated by looking at this figure:[15]

Many people at first see only a random patchwork of black and white areas; but on looking further some people will suddenly see a recognisable figure emerge from the chaos. They suddenly see the head and upper neck of a giraffe. The effect is just as if the giraffe had been switched on, like a light. Most people who do not see it at first for themselves, will do so sooner or later after being told that it is a giraffe. But what happens in this instant of transition? There is evidently no change in the purely sensory experience, i.e. in the sensory stimulus to the organism. The pattern registered on the retina of the eye is the same whether the giraffe is seen or not. There is no change in this pattern at the instant when the giraffe is seen — the actual marks on the page are exactly the same after the event of recognition as they were before. So the difference cannot be explained as a difference in sensory experience.

This conclusion is reinforced by experience with the well-known ambiguous figures used by the gestalt psychologists, such as the reversing cube or the duck/rabbit:

21

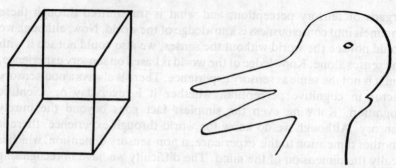

In these cases two different objects can be seen alternately, and yet the pattern of retinal stimulation is the same in both cases. Hanson suggests that what changes in such cases is the organization.[16] He points out that the organization is not itself seen in the same way as the lines or shapes, because it is not itself a line or shape. It is not an element in the visual field which registers on the retina along with other such elements, but "rather the way in which elements are appreciated". Without this organization "we would be left with nothing but an unintelligible configuration of lines", as indeed we are left with nothing but an unintelligible configuration of shapes, a random patchwork of black and white areas, until this becomes organized in the act of seeing a giraffe. But just as the plot is not another detail in the story, or the tune is not just another note, so the giraffe is not another element in the visual field. Although, when it is seen, the shapes now have a particular organization, the change cannot be shewn by making an exact copy of the figure.[17] Two people, one of whom could see the giraffe and the other not, would both produce the very same copies of the figure. The difference between them lies in the non-sensory factor in perception, which is the part of seeing that is "more than meets the eye".

It is now possible to go further than this, and to understand more completely just what it is that we see in cognitive perception. The non-sensory perception of organization which has been discussed above is in fact the perception of meaning. The experience of suddenly seeing the giraffe, for example, is the experience of seeing meaning where previously there had been only a meaningless patchwork of black and white shapes. The non-sensory wholeness or unity which we see in the instant this patchwork becomes organized *is* the meaning 'giraffe'. This is not the meaning *of* what is seen, but the meaning which *is* what is seen. The marks on the page do not 'have' any meaning at all, i.e. the meaning is not on the page as it would have to be if it were a sensory element. So what we are seeing is not in fact on the page, even though it appears to be there. Similarly, the alternation with the duck/rabbit, or the reversing

22

cube, is a switch in the meaning which is seen. In fact, even to see these figures just as 'a set of lines', or 'a patchwork of black and white shapes', is already to see meaning. There cannot be a cognitive perception of meaningless data, because in the act of seeing the world it *is* meaning that we see.[18]

There is no fundamental difference between seeing objects and seeing facts. Seeing that a book is on the table is simply a more complex instance of seeing meaning than seeing a book, or a table, on its own would be. Spatial and temporal relationships, especially those entailing causality, which are so readily believed to be perceived through the senses, are always in fact instances of the non-sensory perception of meaning. For example, suppose that someone hears a whirring noise and, at the same time, sees a helicopter. He knows immediately that the one is the cause of the other, and it seems that this fact is given directly to the senses alone. But no such *connection* could ever be perceived by purely sensory experience. Although we cannot *know* what such a state would be like, it is a useful exercise to try to catch a glimpse of it by suspending meaning. The attempt to do this can bring us to the point of appreciating that purely sensory experience would be a state of difference without distinction, diversity without differentiation. It would be a condition of total multiplicity without any trace of unity, no matter how diluted. In fact, the best way to describe it would be as a state of awareness without meaning. What has previously been referred to as 'a meaningless patchwork of black and white shapes', is in fact meaningful comp. red with this state. The perception which sees 'a meaningless patchwork of black and white shapes' already recognises *unity* in multiplicity, and hence is not seeing pure 'difference without distinction'. Yet we know from pathological and other cases that the state of purely sensory experience does exist, and that it is a state which corresponds to the complete absence of meaning.[19] So the philosophy of empiricism, which believes that knowledge of the world comes directly through the senses, is fundamentally misleading.

The error of empiricism rests on the fact that what it takes to be material objects are condensations of meaning. When we see a chair, for example, we are seeing a condensed meaning and not simply a physical body. Since meanings are not objects of sensory perception, seeing a chair is not the sensory experience we imagine it to be. What empiricism, and common sense, miss through mistaking meaning for matter is the dimension of mind in cognitive perception. The world which we see and know exists in an ocean of mind. But this is usually invisible to us because it is transparent in the act of cognitive perception, and hence we do not suspect that it is there. It is often only in cases where normal cognition is disrupted that the dimension of mind can become visible.

What also hides this dimension from us is the presupposition that cognitive processes can be understood in the framework of the Cartesian divorce of subject from object, the separation of consciousness from world. This presupposition has to be brought into the light and thought through carefully, when it becomes evident that it is inherently incoherent. For much of its history over the past few centuries, Western philosophy has been concerned with the problem of epistemology which arises directly out of this divorce. During this century studies in the philosophy of language and in phenomenology have both, in their different ways, led to a clearer recognition of the incoherence at the root of the Cartesian position and all that follows from its assumption. The work of Edmund Husserl, the founder of phenomenology, has been particularly influential.[20] He identified the mistake of conceiving consciousness in the manner of a natural object, as described by the physical sciences, as if it were an object among other objects in nature. He recognised that it is therefore a mistake to try to imagine an empty consciouness confronting an external world. The fundamental discovery on which phenomenology is based is that consciousness has the structure of *intentionality* — it would be better to say that consciousness *is* intentionality.[21] This is often expressed by saying that consciousness is always 'consciousness of'. In other words, consciousness is a vector because it is always directed towards an object. Hence in cognitive perception there is an indissoluble unity between the conscious mind and the object of which it is conscious. This is completely overlooked by the epistemological approach which is based on the attempt to overcome Cartesian dualism. In fact, it turns out that this approach is another instance of trying to "reach the milk by way of the cheese", because the subject-object distinction on which it is based itself arises out of the process of cognition. But this is not the place to go further into this.

The discovery of the intentionality of consciousness explains the transparency of mind in cognitive perception, and the origin of the empiricist fallacy. Because of its vector nature, consciousness is directed towards the object of cognition. It is this object which occupies attention and not the act of seeing itself. Hence the dimension of the mind is invisible in the normal process of cognition, and the object which is seen appears to have been seen by the senses alone. The picture of the giraffe illustrates this clearly. When the giraffe is seen it appears there on the page, and hence it seems to be seen by means of the senses alone. Yet in this case, as described above, we can learn to recognise that there is no picture of a giraffe on the page.

The discovery of the intentionality of consciousness also makes clear the difference between the meaning which *is* what is seen, and the meaning *of* what is seen. Because of the transparency of mind in cognitive perception, arising from the vector nature of consciouness, the meaning which *is* what is seen becomes invisible as such and appears as something other than it is, namely a sensory object. Hence we are left with only a secondary notion of meaning, namely the meaning *of* what is seen. This is secondary because what is seen *is* meaning already. It is this primary meaning, which is constitutive of what things are, that is overlooked by the Cartesian distinction and the naturalistic attitude of empiricism. As a result of this oversight, there is a temptation on first encountering the phenomenological approach to misread the meaning which *is* what is seen for the meaning *of* what is seen. But once the primary meaning is rediscovered, then the secondary notion of meaning can be recognised as being built on what is meaning already. The difference here is really between the constitutive mind and the reflective mind. But since the former is transparent in cognitive perception, 'mind' is usually identified with the latter alone. However, this is only a secondary function of the mind, which depends on there being a world which is already constituted and can therefore be taken for granted.

It is probably still true that most of us think of scientific knowledge as being somehow fundamentally different from ordinary everyday knowledge. But studies in the philosophy of science have converged with cognitive psychology to show that this is not true. It turns out that the differences are only superficial. There is no fundamental difference in the *process* of cognition, and scientific cognition can be understood as an extension of everyday cognition at a more comprehensive level. Both are concerned with condensations of meaning, and not with sense data directly. The objects of cognitive perception at the level of everyday cognition become the raw data for the higher-level condensation of meaning which is cognition at the scientific level. The transparency of mind in the act of cognition now results in the erroneous view that scientific discoveries are made directly by observations which are entirely sensory. This disappearance of the dimension of mind results in an understanding of science which is upside down. It is this distorted image of scientific knowledge which is presented in textbooks and in the media, and which is communicated tacitly by the very way that science is taught. For example, it is reported that Galileo made a telescope, and that when he looked through it he saw mountains and valleys on the moon, as if this knowledge came to him down the telescope and through his eyes. The account which Galileo himself gave of his observations with the telescope makes it quite clear that to begin with he saw nothing of the kind.[22] With regard to the mountains on the moon, for example, he was at first almost literally in a position very similar to that of looking at the black and white

25

blotches *before* seeing a giraffe. The discovery that there are 'mountains' on the moon was a perception of meaning, and not the purely sensory experience it is represented as being. This single example could be multiplied indefinitely to illustrate the point that is being made here. It is particularly noticeable how the "result" of an experiment may be described as if it had been discovered through the senses. For instance, Newton's experiment with the prism is presented as "showing" that white light consists of a mixture of colours, as if this had been observed. The experiment is first described in terms of the theory, which is the meaning that Newton perceived, and then this description is mistaken for what can be seen with the senses. When meanings are mistaken for sensory data in this way, we have what amounts to the conjuring trick philosophy of science — the rabbit is pulled out of the hat, but only because it was put there in the first place. The difficulty with this is that the "result" of the experiment is invested with a cognitive authority which it does not have.

Discovery in science is always the perception of meaning, and it could not be otherwise. The essence of a discovery is therefore in the non-empirical factor in cognition. The recognition that meaning is a primary datum of cognitive experience brings a considerable simplification to the philosophy of science.[23] Of course, the meaning in question may be several stages removed from the meaning in everyday cognition, and at a much more comprehensive level. Such is the case, for example, with the meanings which are the most widely-embracing scientific theories. But sufficient has now been said about the nature of scientific knowledge for us to be able to understand it more adequately.

2.3.2. Unity without Unification

Once it has been recognised that the unity of the phenomenon is not given in sensory experience, the question arises naturally of whether this unity is simply imposed on the experience of the senses by the mind; or whether it is there in the phenomenon itself and the mind is functioning as an organ of non-sensory perception?

There is no doubt that, to a far greater degree than we usually realize, the mind organizes experience by *imposing* an organizational framework. This may be at a relatively superficial level, such as the social-linguistic organization of our daily lives. Or it may be at a level which is much less immediately accessible, such as the way in which we impose a temporal framework on our experience which organizes it into a linear sequence of moments. We then impose this framework intellectually on nature, with the result that we imagine nature as being organized in a linear temporal sequence, and it then becomes possible to describe motion and change

26

quantitatively. Since the time of Kant's philosophy there has been a growing recognition of this active role of the mind, and of the tendency to mistake our own intellectual constructs for "the way things are".

The recognition of the active role of the intellectual mind gave rise to a philosophy of science which maintained the view that a scientific theory is only a container for the facts. It is an intellectual framework which we construct for holding the facts together for our own convenience — where in this case it is believed that the facts themselves are perceived entirely by the senses, independently of the theory. At the beginning of the century this philosophy of science was developed enthusiastically by Mach, Poincaré and Duhem. Mach, for example, believed that the laws of nature are really only our intellectual mnemonics for reproducing facts in thought, and hence are only convenient summaries of what has been experienced. This philosophy is sometimes called phenomenalism, and it clearly bears a family resemblance to empiricism. It was subsequently developed further in the late 1920's and the 1930's, by combining it with studies in mathematical logic, to form the philosophy of logical empiricism, which is also called logical positivism.[24] In this form it was imported into America by central European intellectuals, where it exerted a considerable influence on attitudes towards research, as well as on science education, during the 1940's and 1950's.[25] But even before this, several of the major figures in the development of physics had been strongly influenced by this philosophy. For example, Einstein said: "The object of all sciences is to coordinate our experiences and to bring them into a logical system"; and Neils Bohr said: "The task of science is both to extend the range of our experience and to reduce it to order." Although these may look like the independent judgements of two individual scientists, they are in fact simply reflections of a prevailing philosophy in the culture of the time.

According to the understanding of the intellectual mind, the unity of experience is produced by unification, i.e. unity *is* unification. It is the synthetic unity of an organisational synthesis. Now this is certainly true for the intellectual mind. But the unity which Goethe perceived in the colour phenomenon is *not* a unity that is imposed by the mind. What Goethe saw was not an intellectual unification but the wholeness of the phenomenon itself. He came to see the wholeness of the phenomenon by consciously experiencing it, and this experience cannot be reduced to an intellectual construction in terms of which the phenomenon is organized. It is not reached by a process of intellectual thought, but by a change of consciousness — this will be discussed in section 2.3.3. The unity which is perceived in this way *is* the phenomenon — but not the phenomenon as it is immediately accessible to the perception of the senses. The perception

27

of this unity is an experience of seeing the phenomenon in depth. But this depth is not an extensive dimension. It can be approximated by saying that the phenomenon is experienced as "standing in its own depth". There is in fact no adequate intellectual equivalent to this experience of an intensive depth in the phenomenon — this will be discussed further in section 2.3.4. By contrast with the intellectual unity which is unification, this unity of the phenomenon itself can be called 'unity without unification'. The experience of seeing this unity *is* the theory for Goethe, for whom the term 'theory' was much closer to the original Greek 'theoria' — which simply means 'seeing'.

The difference between the two kinds of unity discussed here can be expressed in terms of a distinction introduced by Martin Heidegger.[26] He considered two different perspectives of the notion of 'belonging together'. These can be seen as being like the two perspectives of the reversing cube. Just as we see one of these cubes easily but have to make an effort to see the other one, so, with the two perspectives of 'belonging together', one comes easily to us but we have to learn how to see the other.

Heidegger's distinction is made according to whether the emphasis is placed on 'belonging' or 'together'. Thus, in the perspective of 'belonging *together*' he sees the belonging as being determined by the together; whereas in the perspective of '*belonging* together' the reverse is the case, and the together is determined by the belonging. In the first case, he says that 'to belong' means to be placed in the order of a 'together', i.e. a unity which is the unity of an organized system. But in the latter case, '*belonging* together', there is "the possibility of no longer representing belonging in terms of the unity of the together, but rather of experiencing this together in terms of belonging." The perspective of 'belonging *together*' clearly corresponds to the unity which is unification, and this suggests that the perspective of '*belonging* together' corresponds to unity without unification. In terms of this distinction we can say that Goethe perceived the *belonging* together of the colours, instead of trying to make them belong *together*. This is the unity which is perceived in the qualities of the prismatic colours at a boundary, and in the qualities of the colours in Goethe's "instance worth a thousand." For example, in his perception of the primal phenomenon he saw the yellow sun and the blue sky *belonging* together. But, although it may seem that he saw this 'unity without unification' in the sensory world, he did not in fact see it by means of the senses — for which there is only the juxtaposition of these two colour phenomena without any connection or relationship. This unity is within the phenomenon itself, unlike the intellectual unity of unification, but it is not visible to the senses. When we see the sun and the sky, we

28

usually do so separately. Even if we do notice them together we do not experience their colours *belonging* together. We experience the colours of the sun and sky in the mode of separation and not in the mode of their unity. It will be shown below that the difference between these two experiences is a difference in the mode of consciousness, from which it will emerge that 'unity without unification' is the unity of the intuitive mind instead of the unity of the intellectual mind.

It helps to keep in mind the fact that consciousness is a vector, always directed towards the object and not towards itself — as described above in section 2.3.1. Hence this unity is easily experienced *as if* it were also part of the phenomenon perceived through the senses, and hence as if it were observed along with the colours themselves. In fact, we can observe the colours, but we *see* the unity. The unity "lights up" in consciousness — it is an insight and not an "outsight". The phenomenon is only partially visible to the senses. The complete phenomenon is visible only when there is a coalescence of sensory outsight with noetic insight.

2.3.3. Modes of Consciousness

We will now see that the difference between these two perspectives of belonging *together* and *belonging* together, corresponding to the two kinds of unity, can be understood in terms of two different modes of consciousness.

There is now a growing body of evidence to support the view that there are two major modes of human consciousness which are complementary.[27] In our technical-scientific culture we have specialised in the development of only one of these modes, to which our educational system is geared almost exclusively. This is the analytical mode of consciousness, which develops in conjunction with our experience of perceiving and manipulating solid bodies. The internalization of our experience of the closed boundaries of such bodies leads to a way of thinking which naturally emphasises distinction and separation. Since the fundamental characteristic of the world of solid bodies is *externality* — i.e. everything is external to everything else — then this way of thinking is necessarily analytical. For the same reason it is also necessarily sequential and linear, proceeding from one element to another in a piecemeal fashion. Henri Bergson noticed the affinity between logical relations with concepts and spatial relations with solid bodies, and he concluded that "our logic hardly does more than express the most general relations among solids".[28] The principles of logic — identity (A is A), non-contradiction (not at the same time A and not-A), and excluded middle (either A or not-A) — are extrapolations from these limited circumstances which are assumed to hold universally. For this reason the mode of consciousness associated

29

with logical thinking is necessarily analytical.

The analytical mode of consciousness is also associated with language. A basic structure of modern languages is their subject-predicate grammar, which has the effect of dividing experience into separate elements which are then treated as if they existed independently of each other. For example, "I see the tree" seems to entail the external union of a disjoint set of elements comprising subject, object, and the act of seeing which links them together. But the experience indicated by this sentence can only artificially be considered to be put together like this, because in the case of cognitive perception there is no seeing without somebody there to see and something to be seen. It has been noticed often that the effect of such a grammatical structure is to lead to a view of the world as consisting basically of a collection of detached objects, which combine in various ways to produce the different kinds of entities that we encounter.[29] In other words, the grammatical structure of language articulates the world analytically. It discloses the analytical world. But we believe this to be "the way the world is", independently of language, because language itself is transparent in the act of disclosing this world.[30] It is this analytical structure of language which has made it inadequate for describing the domains which have been discovered in modern physics.[31]

Another aspect of the analytical nature of language is seen in its linear, sequential character. For example, the mechanics of writing consists in putting one letter after another, and one word after another, in lines. But this linearity of language can be over-emphasised, and there are non-linear, holistic features of language that can easily be missed. This happens because attention becomes fixed on the level of the word instead of on the level of meaning. The meaning is not present in the same linear manner as the words, and the tension which the writer experiences is between the linearity of the words and the non-linear meaning. Nevertheless, it is inevitable that the linear mechanism of writing, and reading, has the effect of conditioning us into an analytical mode of consciousness. Often what is called the stream of thought is in fact the stream of language, and the process of thinking is none other than the flow of linguistic associations. The analytical mode of consciousness, therefore, corresponds to the discursive thought of what, for completeness, should be called the verbal-intellectual mind.

The holistic mode of consciousness is complementary to this analytical one. By contrast, this mode is non-linear, simultaneous, intuitive instead of verbal-intellectual, and concerned more with relationships than with the discrete elements that are related. It is important to realize that this mode of consciousness, is a way of seeing, and as such it can only be experienced in its own terms. In particular, it cannot be understood by the verbal-intellectual mind because this functions in the analytical mode of consciousness, where it is not possible to appreciate adequately what it means to say that a *relationship* can be experienced as something real in itself. In the analytical mode of consciousness it is the *elements* which are related that stand out in experience, compared with which the relationship is but a shadowy abstraction. The experience of a relationship as such is only possible through a transformation from a piecemeal way of thought to a simultaneous perception of the whole. Such a transformation amounts to a re-structuring of consciousness itself.[32]

It will be shown below how Goethe's way of science leads to just such a re-structuring of consciousness. But before entering into the details of Goethe's scientific consciousness, a more everyday example of what is meant by a transition from an analytical to a holistic mode of consciousness may be useful. When this idea is first introduced, it is often understood in a rather static way — which is itself a characteristic of the analytical mode of consciousness. Thus, lacking the necessary experience, or perhaps just not having noticed it, we try to imagine elements which are experienced simultaneously as if they were present together in a static way, as in a snapshot of a changing scene. In fact the experience of simultaneity and relationship in the holistic mode of consciousness is the opposite of this, inasmuch as it is inherently dynamical. Whereas we imagine movement and change analytically, as if the process really consisted of a linear sequence of instantaneously stationary states (like a sequence of snapshots), when movement and change is experienced holistically it is experienced dynamically as one whole. The elements which are experienced simultaneously in this mode are thus dynamically related to each other, and this *dynamical* simultaneity replaces the static simultaneity of the analytical mode.

Imagine cutting an orange, for example. We see the knife and orange simply as separate entities which are brought together externally in space and sequentially in time. But another way of experiencing this is possible, which is entered into by giving attention to the *act* of cutting the orange, instead of to the separate entities which are brought together. If this is done, the process of cutting can be experienced simultaneously as one whole, as if it were one present moment instead of a linear sequence of instants. Similarly, if we watch a bird flying across the sky and put our attention into seeing flying, instead of seeing a bird which flies (implying a separation between an entity 'bird' and an action 'flying' which it performs), we can experience this in the mode of dynamical simultaneity as one whole event. By plunging into seeing *flying* we find that our attention expands to experience this movement as one whole which is its

31

own present moment.

It becomes evident through doing this kind of exercise that the description of motion and change as a linear sequence of instantaneous states is a device of the intellectual mind, i.e. it is a consequence of being in the analytical mode of consciousness. This analytical framework is very useful for calculating motion and change, i.e. for apprehending it quantitatively, but it does not take us into the reality of movement and change as a mode of being. This can only be experienced holistically, not analytically, and hence only through a change in the mode of consciousness.[33] It is important to realize that this is not a change in the content of consciousness, as if there were some element which previously had been overlooked, but a change in the *mode* of consciousness. This means that the change is in the relationship between the elements, i.e. in their mode of togetherness.

These examples illustrate very clearly the way that the holistic mode of consciousness can be entered into by plunging into looking, which means by the redeployment of attention into sense perception and away from the verbal-intellectual mind. In the case of motion, by directing our attention into sense perception we discover an aspect of motion which is completely different from the way that motion is understood analytically, and which is therefore not included in the way that we have come to understand motion intellectually — which in fact denies the reality of motion. Arthur Deikman has identified this investment of attention in the sensory as a major step in the transition to another mode of consciousness.[34] In his experimental studies of the psychology of meditation, he discovered that "The meditation exercise could be seen as withdrawing attention from thinking and reinvesting it in percepts — a reverse of the normal learning sequence."[35] The normal learning sequence which is referred to here is called the process of automatization. This is the transference of attention from the sensory experience to the mental abstraction. After this has happened, the sensory occurrence is always experienced tinged with the mental abstraction, or even "tuned out" altogether — so that what we "experience" is only an abstraction, in which case we are completely automatized and in fact no longer different from any complex machine.[36] It is this process which contemplative meditation reverses by reinvesting attention in the sensory experience, and thus withdrawing it from the mental abstraction — and from thinking in general, this being often no more than a process of associating such abstractions via the medium of language which encapsulates them. For this reason, Deikman identifies meditation as an exercise of the attention for producing *deautomatization* of the psychological structures organizing experience, especially the logical organization of consciousness — which has been identified here, following Ornstein, as the analytical mode of consciousness.

This is the key to the psychology of Goethe's way of science. He was doing science and not meditation. But if we look at the psychological process, instead of the nominal identification, we can recognize that Goethe's way of science and meditation share the common factor of deautomatization and the transformation of consciousness. In the description of Goethe's work on colour, in section 2.2, we distinguished two stages in the encounter with the phenomenon. First there is the observation stage, which is characterized by active seeing instead of the passive reception of visual impressions. This entails putting attention into seeing, plunging into seeing the qualities of the colours. Doing this takes us into the phenomenon, but at the same time it takes attention away from the verbal-intellectual mind and hence promotes deautomatization from the analytical mode of consciousness. The intellectual mind is concerned with uniformity. For example, in the case of say, two leaves, it is concerned with only what is common to them — that they are both instances of 'leaf' — and overlooks the individual differences between them. In contrast to the intellectual mind, the world of sensory experience is non-uniform and endlessly varied and rich in diversity. Hence, investing attention in the sensory inevitably promotes deautomatization from the uniformity of the intellectual mind. The second stage in Goethe's way, the stage he called exact sensorial imagination, takes this process further. It deepens both the encounter with the phenomenon and the process of deautomatization. The attempt to think the phenomenon in imagination, and not to think about it, is sensory and not intellectual, concrete and not abstract. Attention is thereby further withdrawn from verbal associations and intellectual reasoning. This, therefore, is a deautomatization exercise. But at the same time it is an exercise in trying to see the phenomenon in the simultaneous mode, i.e. all at once. Hence, as well as undoing the usual construction of consciousness by the redirection of attention — which by itself can be sufficient for the other mode of consciousness to emerge — this exercise actively promotes the re-structuring of consciousness into an organ of holistic perception.[37]

This psychological interpretation of Goethe's way of access to nature in terms of deautomatization is reinforced by considering the subjective experience of the procedure. Through trying to direct attention into the act of looking, we can experience for ourselves the gap which there is between our habitual awareness and the direct experience of what is there in front of us. It is only when this hiatus in experience is overcome that we realize how little we usually perceive directly of the concrete detail of the

33

particular. We usually classify verbally and experience just a vague generality. A striking feature of this attempt to give attention to active looking and exact sensorial imagination is how much subjective resistance it can set up in a person. This in itself is an indication that the orientation which it calls for is towards deautomatization or dishabituation. This subjective effect is an instance of the psychological inertia which has to be matched by a person's own activity if the state of his or her awareness is to change, just as the inertia of a material body has to be matched by a force if its state of motion is to be changed.

When consciousness is thus re-structured into an organ of holistic perception, the mind functions intuitively instead of intellectually. There is a lot of confusion and misunderstanding about intuition, as if it were something intangible and mysterious. But in fact it is a very clear and precise notion. Ornstein defines intuition as "knowledge without recourse to inference".[38] He links it with a simultaneous perception of the whole, whereas the logical or rational mode of knowledge "involves an analysis into discrete elements sequentially (inferentially) linked".[39] He connects the intuitive mind with the holistic mode of consciousness — as the intellectual mind is linked with the analytical mode. Thus, intuition is connected with a change of consciousness, and moreover in a way which can be made quite precise and not just left vague. It now follows that Goethe's procedures are practical exercises for educating the mind to function intuitively instead of intellectually, leading to a science which is intuitive instead of organized intellectually.[40]

It can now be seen that 'unity without unification' is possible in the holistic mode of consciousness, whereas unity by means of unification is the characteristic of the analytical mode of consciousness. But because the former is literally a matter of seeing with the mind, i.e. insight, it can easily be mistaken for the sensory. This is why it was necessary to establish first (in section 2.3.1) that knowledge is not achieved by the senses alone. There is always a non-sensory element in knowledge, and this must be so whether this element is verbal-intellectual or intuitive. The difference is that, whereas the verbal-intellectual mind withdraws from the sensory aspect of the phenomenon into abstraction and generality, the intuitive mind goes into and through the sensory surface of the phenomenon to perceive it in its own depth. It is by first going into the full richness and diversity of sensory detail that the intellectual mind is rendered ineffective, so that we can escape from its prison into the freedom of intuition.

2.3.4. The Depth of the Phenomenon

Etymologically, 'intuition' means 'seeing into', which clearly expresses

34

the fact that it is the experience of seeing the phenomenon in depth. But this depth is peculiar inasmuch as it is entirely within the phenomenon and not behind it — so it should be understood as an intensive dimension, and not in the manner of an extensive dimension of physical space. It is in fact the depth of the phenomenon itself. It is as if something which appears to be two-dimensional suddenly turns out to be three-dimensional, so that what had seemed flat is now seen in relief. This is the experience mentioned earlier (in section 2.3.2.) of seeing the phenomenon "standing in its own depth". It was said then that there is no intellectual equivalent to this experience, and the reason for this is now clearly because it is an intuitive experience which depends on a change of consciousness.

When the phenomenon is seen intuitively it has a further dimension to it, but this does not change the particular elements in the phenomenon. It changes the way that the elements are related, and hence their significance, but they remain the same elements so far as the senses as concerned. For example, the blue of the sky and yellow of the sun are, in a clearly recognizable way, the same elements when they are seen *belonging* together in the holistic mode, as they are when seen analytically as just two separate and contingent facts. In the former case there is a depth in the phenomenon which is entirely absent in the latter. This intensive depth which is seen intuitively in the holistic mode of consciousness *is* the wholeness of the phenomenon. The authentic unity of the phenomenon (i.e. unity without unification) is literally a further dimension of the phenomenon itself, which is seen as such only when the mind functions in the intuitive mode of 'seeing into'.

The intellectual mind misses this dimension, because it is not visible in the analytical mode of consciousness, and therefore must compensate for what is missing by adding on its own thought construction to the phenomenon as it is presented to sensory experience. This has usually been done in physics by constructing an explanatory model. It has already been mentioned (in section 2.1) how Newton tried to construct such a model for light. This method of explanation by mechanical models was the classical way in physics from Descartes onwards, until its validity was called into question this century by the development of the quantum theory.[41] It was depicted in a memorable way by Einstein and Infeld. They ask us to imagine a watch which is being examined by a man who has never encountered a watch before, and who therefore does not know what it is. They also ask us to imagine that this watch is impregnable, so that no matter what he does he cannot open it and look inside. This picture is offered as a parallel to the situation of the scientific investigator with regard to the phenomena of nature. The man can investigate the watch through his senses and his mind, until he discovers the "law of the watch", i.e. the pattern of the movement of the hands. But he cannot open it up to discover the mechanism which produces this pattern. "If he is ingenious he may form some picture of the mechanism which could be responsible for all the things he observes, but he may never be quite sure his picture is the only one which could explain his observations."[42] Similarly with the actual scientific investigator, he can discover the regularities in the phenomena of nature, i.e. the so-called laws of nature, but he cannot open nature up to look inside. He cannot go behind the scenes to discover something hidden which produces the observed regularities. So at this point he must try to construct a picture of a hidden mechanism which would give rise to the phenomenon observed with the senses.

This metaphor for the intellectual step from observation to theory is clearly very limited, and in terms of the contemporary philosophy of science it is also very naive. But, in spite of this, it must be taken seriously because of what is communicated by its form. This communicates the view that there is another world hidden behind the world we experience with the senses, and that it is this *other* world which is the physical cause of the world that we experience directly. Now this is a very widespread assumption and, without going into detail, there are some aspects of it which need to be brought out explicitly. Firstly, this other world is conceived in a spatial manner, as if it were like the world of our bodily experience only hidden. So here too the phenomenon is conceived as having a depth to it, but this is an *extended* depth *behind* the phenomenon. Secondly, this other world hidden behind the scenes is pictured as being like the sensory world which it explains, in so far as the kinds of things which it contains are imagined as sensory-like elements, such as light waves for example. Thirdly, there is no direct access to this backstage world, and it can be approached only by means of the intellectual mind in terms of mental constructions and representations. But, because this world also contains sensory-like elements, albeit invisible ones, there is no reason in principle why it should not be directly visible if we had developed the necessary sense organs. All of this can be summarized simply by saying that this is how the depth of the phenomenon is conceived by the intellectual mind in the analytical mode of consciousness, and hence according to the logic of solid bodies. In other words, it is a superficial projection of what the depth of the world is like, because it is literally a fanciful projection of the surface into the depth.

This helps, by contrast, to bring out more clearly the nature of Goethe's discovery. He would strenuously deny that there is another world hidden behind the sensory world in this way. Any such dualism was repugnant to him. What he saw was a depth in the phenomenon which is another dimension of *the same phenomenon* that is experienced with the senses. There is nothing backstage. There is only the phenomenon itself, but this has another dimension to it, a further aspect which is not a sensory element at all. This is the dimension of wholeness, which is the unity of the phenomenon. For Goethe, the theory *is* seeing this intensive dimension of the phenomenon. This is much closer to the original greek 'theoria', which simply means 'seeing'. The phenomenon is not seen in another dimension by the senses, and not by the sightless fancies of the verbal-intellectual mind. It is seen intuitively by a change of consciousness. But it has to be remembered all the time that, when the phenomenon is seen in this dimension, the elements are the same as in the sensory phenomenon — the difference is in the way that they are related. It is the transformation in their mode of togetherness, which is experienced intuitively through a change of consciousness, which gives the phenomenon its intensive depth.

Now it is possible to understand better the meaning of some of Goethe's occasional remarks about the relationship between fact and theory:

"Let the facts themselves speak for their theory."

"Don't look for anything behind the phenomena; they themselves are the theory."

"The greatest achievement would be to understand that everything factual is already its own theory."

It is easy to misinterpret these remarks by failing to realize that they refer to the phenomenon as it is experienced by the intuitive mind, and by trying to understand them with the intellectual mind alone. For example, it would be possible to produce a rational reading of what Goethe is saying here by making an association with the discovery by the contemporary philosophy of science, which is corroborated by the psychology of perception, that scientific observation is always theory-laden.[43] It would also be possible to produce another, equally rational, reading by making an association with the kind of phenomenalism developed by Ernst Mach which was mentioned in Section 2.3.2. In this case they would be interpreted as saying that the theory reduces to the facts, as if it were nothing more than merely the facts themselves. But what Goethe is saying goes in the opposite direction to this. He says this is something *to be achieved*. The facts are to be raised to the level of being theory, and not the other way round. But when this is achieved they are still the same facts. They have been transformed, but they have not been

37

changed into something different. This can readily be seen by considering the two separate facts that the sun is yellow and the sky is blue, and the way that these are transformed when they are seen *belonging* together in the mode of unity without unification.

Goethe's remarks about the relationship between fact and theory become transparent when the phenomenon is experienced intuitively in its own depth, They simply describe what this experience is like. The theory *is* the facts when these are seen in another dimension. This perception is attained by a change of consciousness and not by a process of rational thought. Seen in one mode, the analytical, the facts are merely the facts; seen in the other mode, the holistic, they *are* the theory.

This transformation from an analytical to a holistic mode of consciousness brings with it a reversal between the container and the content. What is encountered in the theory is, for Goethe, the real content of the phenomenon, for which the sensory facts are now merely the container. This is in contrast to the analytical mode for which the sensory facts are the content of the phenomenon. In the case of phenomenalism and positivism, it has been mentioned already (in section 2.3.2.) that the theory is considered to be only a container for the facts. Now if the theory, in Goethe's sense, is the real content of the phenomenon, then it can be said that in the moment of intuitive insight we are seeing *inside* the phenomenon. But this 'inside' is very different from that which is imagined by the intellectual mind, and which is depicted by Einstein's watch analogy. The 'inside' of the phenomenon which is imagined by rational thought is a fiction based on our own bodily experience in the external world of bodies. In this case 'inside' is really thought of in an outside kind of way. Hegel saw that the world of bodies is essentially the *external* world.[44] He did not mean by this that it is external to consciousness in a Cartesian sense, because consciousness is not in space and therefore no thing can be outside of it. Hegel meant that the external world is a world which is characterized and permeated by externality, so that it is the world in which everything is outside everything else. So in the mode of thought which is based on our experience of this world it is inevitable that 'inside' is conceived externally. Hence the 'inside' of the world which the intellectual mind imagines is really an outside in disguise. Contrary to this, Goethe's intuitive way of science goes inside the phenomenon to find that it is the *same* phenomenon in another dimension. This is the intensive depth of the phenomenon, and hence the *intensive* inside instead of the extensive 'inside' which is characteristic of the external world. It could therefore be said that, in knowing the phenomenon, Goethe dwells within it consciously instead of replacing it with mental constructs — although equally it could be said that the phenomenon itself dwells in Goethe's scientific consciousness.[45]

The effect of this shift from the intellectual to the intuitive mind is that the phenomenon becomes its own explanation. It discloses itself in terms of itself and thereby becomes self-explanatory. In the terminology of modern philosophy, Goethe's intuitive way of science is a phenomenology of nature, where this term must now be understood in the sense in which it is used by Heidegger.[46] He returns to the Greek word *phainomenon*, which he says gives the fundamental meaning of phenomenon as "that which shows itself in itself". He emphasises that this is not to be confused with the mere appearance of something. The phenomenon is not what is immediately visible. Combining this with his interpretation of the meaning of the Greek word *logos*, Heidegger tells us that phenomenology, as a method of investigation, means "to let that which shows itself be seen from itself in the very way in which it shows itself from itself." Clearly such an approach is the very opposite of an intellectual analysis which imposes its own categories on the phenomenon to organize it subjectively. This description of phenomenology seems cumbersome, and it is a source of irritation to those philosophers who insist that if something cannot be said simply in English then it must be muddled. Yet it describes the *experience* of Goethe's way of science precisely, and thus enables us to identify this philosophically as a phenomenology of nature.

But it is possible to be more specific about this phenomenology. The effect of this event of phenomenological disclosure is that the phenomenon becomes its own language. This is the concrete, non-verbal language which things are. It is important to realize that 'language' is being used literally here and not metaphorically. This confusion can arise because language is usually identified with the verbal language of the intellectual mind, which is a consequence of being restricted to the analytical mode of consciousness. In fact this is really only a special case of language. As well as the meaning that belongs to the intellectual mind, which is verbal, there is the meaning that belongs to the intuitive mind, which is non-verbal and can only be perceived in a holistic mode of consciousness. Nevertheless, both of these are linguistic. Whilst there can be meaning which is non-verbal, there cannot be meaning which is non-linguistic for much the same kind of reason that there cannot be a triangle which is not three-sided. Non-verbal meaning can only be perceived intuitively and not intellectually. We can only approximate to this verbally, in an imperfect way, by saying that non-verbal language is the concrete language which things *are* when they are experienced as *being* language. So it could therefore be said that Goethe learned to read the language of colour. It will be shown in section 3 how he learned to read the plant in terms of itself, so that the plant becomes its own language, and similarly how it is possible to learn to read the language of animal form so that the animal becomes its own explanation. In view of this, Goethe's intuitive way of science can be recognized as a concrete illustration of Gadamer's principle of universal hermeneutics that "being that can be understood is language".[47] The philosophy of Goethe's science can therefore be identified more precisely as the hermeneutic phenomenology of nature.

The difference between Goethe's phenomenological way and the mainstream of mathematical physics from Newton onwards, was summarized memorably and concisely by Cassirer: "The mathematical formula strives to make the phenomena calculable, that of Goethe to make them visible."[48] Taken at its face value this would certainly seem an odd thing to say, because we would usually take it that the phenomena are visible already and so there is no need to strive to make them visible. But now we can appreciate what is being said here. Goethe's way makes the phenomenon visible intuitively, and not just to the senses. Whereas the phenomenon is only partly visible to the senses, it is brought fully into the light by the intuition which perceives the intensive depth and not just the sensory surface. The key to this is the transformation of consciousness into the holistic mode. Then the phenomenon is seen wholly, and hence completely instead of only partly. Of course, this does not mean that the complete phenomenon is the sum of two parts. It is an original unity which is experienced by us partly through the senses and partly through the intuitive consciousness. It was a remarkable insight of Steiner's to recognize that this is a consequence of the way that the human being is organized, and not the result of a division in the phenomenon itself.[49] In other words, there is no dualism in nature. It only appears so to us because of the way in which we ourselves, as human beings, are involved in the process of knowing. What this means is that the phenomenon as it appears to the senses is only an abstraction. This is a reversal of our usual way of thinking, for which what is given to the senses is concrete and what is present to the mind is an abstraction — which of course it is to the intellectual mind.

The difference between the intuitive and intellectual approaches to the science of nature is illustrated metaphorically by Edwin Abbott's story *Flatland*.[50] This concerns a society of creatures who inhabit a two-dimensional surface, and what happens when a sphere appears to one of them. Of course, he is unable to perceive a sphere. All that his sensory experience tells him, as the sphere passes through the plane of his existence, is that a point appears, grows into a circle of expanding

40

diameter, until this becomes a maximum size and then shrinks back to a point again and vanishes. Evidently, what his senses tell him is an abstraction. The sphere tells him that he must go upward. Not having any experience of 'upward', he tries to interpret it at first in terms of his familiar experience with a compass as 'northward'. After struggling for some time with the paradox, to him, of how to go "upward, yet not northward", the sphere casts him out of Flatland into the three-dimensional world. Now he sees directly what he had previously only been able to infer by association based on his familiar experience in the two-dimensional surface. This is a transformation of his consciousness. With the difference that the further dimension in this case is extensive and not intensive, this can be taken as a metaphor for the re-structuring of consciousness into the holistic, intuitive mode that is necessary for the Goethean phenomenologist of nature to be able to make the phenomenon visible.

3. Goethe's Organic Vision

Now that the structure of Goethe's scientific consciousness has been described, it is not difficult to begin to understand his way of seeing organic nature. Patterns of relationships which seem strange, even unconvincing, to the analytical mind begin to fall into place when understood in terms of a holistic mode of consciousness. When this is followed through, it brings us to the point of being able to see the essence of Goethe's organic vision for ourselves.

3.1. The Unity of the Plant

Goethe's best known contribution to biology is undoubtedly his work on the flowering plant, as described in his essay *The Metamorphosis of Plants*, and in some other fragmentary comments dispersed throughout his writings. The flowering plant is usually described in elementary botany books as if it were an external assemblage of different parts — leaves, sepals, petals, stamens, etc. — which are separate and independent of each other. There is no hint of any necessary relationship between them. This is the analytical plant — the plant as it appears to the intellectual mind in the analytical mode of consciousness. It is the plant in Flatland. Linnaeus produced his system for organizing the plants into species, genera, etc. on the basis of comparing these parts of the plant as they occur in different specimens. In contrast to this, Goethe saw the plant holistically. He discovered another dimension in the plant, an intensive depth, in which these different organs are intimately related. In fact, he discovered that they are really all one and the same organ. When we can see the way in which he saw this, then we can understand what he meant by the idea of metamorphosis.

What Goethe discovered in the flowering plant could be described simply as continuity of form. He began *The Metamorphosis of Plants* with the statement that "Anyone who observes even a little the growth of plants will easily discover that certain of their external parts sometimes undergo a change and assume, either entirely, or in greater or lesser degree, the form of the parts adjacent to them."[51] He goes on to describe the anomalous case of a plant which makes a retrograde step and reverses the normal order of growth. Thus, in the case of a double flower, petals

42

develop in the place of stamens and anthers, and in some cases it is possible to recognize in the extra petals traces of their origin as stamens in the normal simple flower. It is in such cases, Goethe believed, that the laws of growth and transformation which are hidden in the normal course of Nature are made more readily visible to intuition. What we learn in this way, and can then recognize in normal growth, is that Nature "produces one part out of another and creates the most varied forms by the modification of one single organ."[52]

The question is: what is this single organ whose modifications appear as the different visible organs? Paradoxically, it is everywhere visible and nowhere visible. Goethe called it the *Urorgan*, which has been variously translated as the archetypal organ, the primal organ, or the organ type. What it must not be confused with is the notion of a primitive organ, as if the *Urorgan* were an especially simple organ out of which other organs develop materially in time. To think of the archetypal organ in this way is to look at it through Darwinian spectacles, and so fail to recognize that Goethe was seeing the plant in another dimension to space and time.

Cassirer recognized that a unique feature of Goethe's way of science is to be found in the relationship between the particular and the universal which it expresses. He said: "There prevails in his writings a relationship of the particular to the universal such as can hardly be found elsewhere in the history of philosophy or of natural science."[53] We are accustomed to thinking of the universal as if it were a generalization made inductively from several particular instances. In this case we imagine going from the particular instances to the universal, which, because it is now identified with the general, appears to be an abstraction. It is in fact an abstraction of the intellectual mind. But Goethe worked to awaken the intuitive mind, for which the universal is not the same as the general, and which is therefore not reached by abstracting the common denominator from several particular instances. For the intuitive mind there is a reversal of perception here. Instead of a movement of mental abstraction from the particular to the general, there is a perception of the universal reflected in the particular. In this moment of reversal the particular is seen in the light of the universal, and hence it appears as a concrete manifestation of the universal. In other words, the particular becomes symbolic of the universal. So what is merely particular to the senses, and the mode of thought which corresponds to them, is simultaneously universal to an intuitive way of seeing which is associated with a different mode of consciousness.

Goethe's description of the primal phenomenon as "an instance worth a thousand, bearing all within itself" has to be understood in terms of this relationship between the universal and the particular. This is also the way that the archetypal plant organ has to be understood — which is why it can be said to be everywhere visible and nowhere visible. Goethe experienced this organ directly with the intuitive perception of the holistic mode of consciousness, and so it must not be confused with a mental abstraction — which is all that it would be for the intellectual mind. Also, as mentioned previously, the archetypal organ must not be confused with a primitive organ from which other organs have developed materially in time. The *Urorgan* is neither internally subjective (a mental abstraction) nor externally objective (a primitive organ). Both of these errors have been made from time to time, and it may even be that Goethe had to work his way through one of them himself (the primitive organ error) before he recognized that what he was looking for would never be found where he was looking for it — or rather, in the *way* that he was looking.

In his botanical notes made on his Italian journey, Goethe wrote: "Hypothesis: All is leaf. This simplicity makes possible the greatest diversity."[54] The leaf he refers to here is to be understood in the universal sense as an omnipotential form and not as a particular physical leaf. The different organs of the plant are then perceived as the metamorphic variations of this form, each of which could be derived from any of the others. There is continuity of form, but not of material substance. Thus a petal can be understood as a metamorphosis of a stem leaf, a stamen can be understood as a metamorphosis of a petal, and so on until all the organs are understood as metamorphic variations of one single organ, which nowhere appears as a physical organ but is visible everywhere to the intuition which sees the universal in the particular. Thus the 'leaf' in "All is leaf" should be understood as a concrete universal, compared to which any particular plant organ is only an abstraction. Goethe tried to avoid the confusion which follows inevitably from seeing this statement in the wrong way, literally instead of intuitively, by suggesting that the organs of the plant should be visualized in metamorphic sequence backwards as well as forwards. Thus, for example, a petal should be seen as a metamorphosis of a stamen equally well as a stamen can be seen as a metamorphosis of a petal. In this way he tried to compensate for the fact that there is no general term with which to designate the diversely metamorphosed organ which *is* the flowering plant. By performing this as an exercise of exact sensorial imagination, we can come to recognize for ourselves that Goethe was describing the plant in another dimension to space and time.

It is an extraordinary experience to look at a flowering plant and see it in Goethe's way. Organs which can be quite different in outer appearance are recognized as being manifestations of the same form, so that the plant now appears as the repeated expression of the same organ — which nowhere appears externally as such. Seeing the plant intuitively in this way is to experience it 'coming into being', instead of analysing the plant as it appears in its finished state. In terms of the category of wholeness, the statement that "All is leaf" becomes an expression of the principle of wholeness that the whole is reflected or disclosed in the part.[55] We would therefore also say that in the moment of intuitive perception the leaf becomes "an instance worth a thousand, bearing all within itself". Many of the themes which have been discussed already in connection with colour can also now be recognized in Goethe's way of seeing the plant. Thus, he made the plant visible in terms of itself, so that "it shows itself in itself". So the plant is seen in another dimension, standing in its own depth. This intensive depth is the wholeness of the plant, which is the unity without unification in which the various organs of the flowering plant *belong* together. Thus the factual plant is disclosed as being its own theory, so that the plant becomes its own language.

Whereas Linnaeus was concerned with making the plant manageable, for the purpose of organizing gardens, Goethe was concerned with making the plant visible. Linnaeus therefore imposed an organization on the plant so that each specimen had a place in a system, whereas Goethe let the plant speak for itself. This is the difference between the intellectual mind and the intuitive mind, which in this case can be linked very clearly with the difference between the analytical and holistic modes of consciousness. In the one way the plant which is observed with the senses is covered over, whereas in the other way it is made more deeply visible. It is only in this latter way that the metamorphosis becomes visible. This is perceived holistically as a relationship within the plant with the quality of necessity. There are some plants where the metamorphosis of the organs is more open, whereas in others it is more hidden. It was through the pathological cases, such as the retrogressive metamorphosis mentioned earlier, that Goethe finally came to see the growth of the flowering plant in terms of the metamorphosis of a single organ. But there are also cases of regular metamorphosis where it is especially visible. A particularly good example is the white water-lily, where the transformation of petals into stamens occurs in stages, so that several different phases can be seen simultaneously.[56] Yet in no case does a petal materially turn into a stamen. The metamorphosis, in Goethe's usage, is not a causal relationship in the mechanical sense. Because our idea of continuity is often superficial — being no more than an extrapolation from our sensory experience of material change — metamorphosis can appear at first more like a discontinuity. It is in fact a deeper continuity, the continuity of form, which can only become visible to intuition.[57]

45

3.1.2. The One and the Many

Goethe's intuition of the fundamental unity of the plant, as expressed in the metamorphic variations of the archetypal organ, was gradually extended to the plant kingdom as a whole. He came to believe that there must be an *Urpflanze*, a primal or archetypal plant, whose metamorphic variations are what we see as all the many different plants. He wrote, after visiting the Botanical Gardens at Padua, that "the thought becomes more and more living that it may be possible out of one form to develop all plant forms." It seems that at first Goethe believed this would be some kind of primitive plant which he could hope to encounter if he searched diligently enough. He imagined it as an especially simple plant out of which other plants would develop materially in time. Eventually, as with the archetypal organ, he understood that the *Urpflanze* would never be found in the way that he was looking for it. When he finally experienced the archetypal plant, whilst in the Botanical Gardens at Palermo, it was through the organ of imagination.[58] He described this experience in his notebooks: "When I closed my eyes and bent my head representing to myself a flower right at the centre of the organ of sight, new flowers sprung out of this heart, with coloured petals and green leaves..... There was no way of stopping the effusion, that went on as long as my contemplation lasted, neither slowing nor accelerating." Subsequently he wrote to Herder that with the archetypal plant it would be possible "to invent plants *ad infinitum*; they would be consistent; that is to say, though non-existing, they would be capable of existing, being no shades or semblances of the painter or poet, but possessing truth and necessity."

It is clear from these descriptions that the archetypal plant which Goethe experienced is not to be confused with a mental abstraction, as if it were a sort of lowest common denominator of all plants. But this error is just as common as the error of supposing the archetypal plant to be a primitive organism. Thus, it is supposed that Goethe started with finished plants as they were presented to him in the environment, and by comparing them externally with one another he abstracted what was common to them to produce a generalization. In this way, it is supposed, he found unity in multiplicity. To begin with he would probably have had to do this with several sets of different plants, producing a generalization for each. Then he would have produced a generalization of these generalizations until he reached the ultimate generalization, the ultimate unity in multiplicity, which would be the archetypal plant. Then perhaps Goethe made the mistake of hypostatizing this ultimate mental abstraction — in much the same sort of way that it is often believed Plato did — and imagined it standing behind the world of the physical plants in a separate world of pure form. In other words, it is supposed that Goethe was overcome by "the logic of solid bodies" when he considered that the archetypal plant was somehow real.

The process of comparing external appearances to find what is common to them is the way that the analytical mode of consciousness tries to find unity. But the unity of this 'unity in multiplicity' has the quality of uniformity, and hence it is static and inflexible. In this mode of consciousness we refer to *reducing* multiplicity to unity. This is the mechanical unity of a pile of bricks, and not the organic unity of life. But Goethe did not begin by making an external comparison of different plants. His own account shows that he worked with his mind in a different way to this. As he was able to see into the individual plant to perceive it holistically, so now he saw into all the plants holistically. He saw into the coming-into-being of the plants so deeply that he saw all plants as one plant. What he saw could be described as 'the possibility of plant'. A philosopher of being like Martin Heidegger would perhaps have said that Goethe reached the 'to be' of plant. The archetypal plant as an omnipotential form is clearly a different dimension of the plant to what appears in the space-time dimension as many plants. To the analytical mind which is formed around experience with material bodies this must seem unreal, and hence must appear to be only an abstract thought. But the phenomenologist of nature does not argue with the phenomenon he encounters! Instead, he looks into his own mind to winkle out the prejudgements and presuppositions which are making him think the phenomenon is unreal. It is not the proper business of intellectual thought to prescribe what is real and what is not, because what seems unreal in one mode of consciousness may not seem so in another.

The omnipotential form which is the archetype is one plant which is all possible plants. As such it is not a blueprint for plants, a general plant, or the common factor in all plants. This, as we have seen, would have the quality of uniformity. But the archetypal plant has the quality of diversity within unity, and from Goethe's own account it is inherently dynamical and indefinitely flexible. The intellectual mind does not understand omnipotentiality dynamically in terms of the coming-into-being of the plants, but statically in terms of the plants that have already become. It conceives it as if it were a state which already contained the finished plants beforehand. This is an analytical counterfeit of something which can only be understood holistically. It is yet another instance of trying to "reach the milk by way of the cheese". Another analytical counterfeit of the omnipotential form, which is also an example of this habit of mind, is the attempt to conceive of it as some kind of synthetic assemblage. A notorious instance of this is found in Turpin's attempt to depict Goethe's archetypal plant pictorially. He drew a picture of a composite plant in

47

which he placed, on one main axis, as many different kinds of leaves as were known, and then showed examples of different kinds of flowers as parts of a single flower. Agnes Arber described this as "a botanist's nightmare, in which features which could not possibly coexist, are forced into the crudest juxtaposition".[59]

The unity of the archetypal plant is inside-out to the unity of 'unity in multiplicity'. The unity of this 'one plant which is many' is better described as 'multiplicity in unity'. This has to be understood intensively, not extensively, so as to avoid implying the contradiction that unity is divided.[60] What this means is that, whereas extensively there are many plants, intensively there is only one plant because each plant *is* the very same one — yet without being identical in the extensive sense, i.e. like a number of copies. It is an exercise in active imagination to go from multiplicity in unity to unity in multiplicity and back again. This difference cannot possibly be understood by the analytical mind. But the imagination can be used to give a sense of turning inside-out from the intensive dimension of the pre-numerical 'one which is many' to the extensive dimension of numerical multiplicity where there are many single ones. For the sake of clarity, the intensive dimension of 'one which is many' (multiplicity in unity) will be written with a capital letter as the intensive dimension of One, to distinguish it from the extensive dimension of many ones (unity in multiplicity). Thus 'One' is a pre-numerical intensive dimension, whereas 'one' is a numerically single individual.[61]

A model for multiplicity in unity is provided by the hologram. Holography is a special kind of photography performed with the light of the laser. The hologram of an object is a photographic plate or film which enables a fully three-dimensional optical reconstruction of the object to appear when it is suitably illuminated. What appears on the plate bears no resemblance whatsoever to the object being holographed. But when the film is looked through it seems as if the object were there in the space behind. It looks as if the three-dimensional visual appearance of the object had been lifted off it, like a skin, and put there in the space behind the film. There are several unusual features of the hologram, but the one which is relevant here concerns what happens if the film is divided into, say, two parts. With a conventional photograph the picture would be divided, with a different part of the photographed object appearing on each bit of the film. But when a hologram film is divided, the whole object is optically reconstructed through each part. The division of the hologram materially is an extensive operation — each part getting smaller and smaller. But the division of the hologram optically is intensive — it is divisible and yet remains whole, producing multiplicity in unity. Whereas

48

there are many holograms materially (many ones), there is One hologram optically (the One which is' many) because each is the very same One. Instead of just following this with the verbal intellectual mind, for which understanding can often be no more than recognizing the meaning of the words, it is better to approach this as an exercise in visualization so that it becomes more of an adventure in perception.

It is through the use of the power of visualization, as in the process of exact sensorial imagination, that the transition can be made from the analytical to the holistic mode of consciousness. We have seen already how this exercise leads to deautomatization from the verbal-intellectual mind which is associated with the analytical mode of consciousness. The unity of the plant kingdom can only appear to this mode of consciousness as unity in multiplicity. This is the extensive perspective of unity. The intensive perspective of unity, which is multiplicity in unity, can only be seen in the holistic mode of consciousness. The common failure to appreciate what Goethe meant by the archetypal plant can be traced to this difference. A lot of confusion has arisen generally in the history of philosophy through attempting to understand unity in the wrong mode of consciousness. Plato's theory of Forms, for example, is almost invariably approached analytically in terms of unity in multiplicity. It is this which leads to the notorious difficulties with his theory of "one over many".[62] The same can be said about the medieval dispute about the nature of universals and the argument between nominalism and realism. Plato's theory of Forms, and the problem of universals, become quite different when approached holistically in terms of multiplicity in unity and the intensive dimension of One. Philosophers like to proceed by the way of logical argument, but it could be that it is the mode of consciousness associated with this way which is responsible for some of the conundrums which they are thereby trying to resolve.

It is now possible to clarify the difference between the general and the universal which was referred to earlier in this section. It is clear that the general has the structure of unity in multiplicity, since it is what is common to many particular instances. The universal has the structure of multiplicity in unity, and is not reached by standing back from many instances to get an overview but by a change of consciousness. In this case the One is seen reflected in the many, so that the many are seen in the light of One instead of trying to evaporate one off from the many as a mental abstraction — which is sometimes referred to as reducing the many to the one. The universal is therefore the unity of the intuitive mind. The general is the unity of the intellectual mind, and so it is the intellectual mind's counterfeit for the universal. The difference can be summarized in a diagram:

49

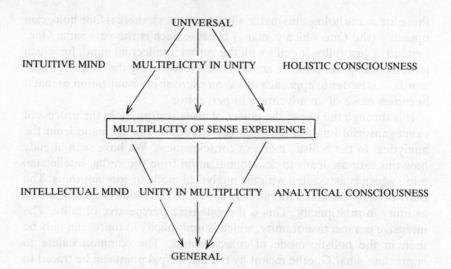

Goethe's archetypes, like Plato's Forms, belong with the intuitive mind and should not be confused with intellectual concepts. His notion of the primal phenomenon as "an instance worth a thousand, bearing all within itself" is to be understood in the same way. Throughout his life Goethe gradually had to emancipate himself from the idol of empiricism.[63] To begin with he thought of his work on colour empirically in the manner laid down by Francis Bacon. But he came to think subsequently that Bacon's method of inductive generalization from many individual cases was lifeless.[64] He pointed out the limitation in Bacon's approach: that complicated cases were necessarily given the same weight at first as simple cases — though, of course, there would be no way beforehand of knowing which was which. He believed that it would be impossible in practice to proceed in the way that Bacon advocated, and instead he gradually developed his own way of looking for "an instance worth a thousand, bearing all within itself". The method which Bacon advocated clearly has the form of looking for unity in multiplicity. Goethe's way is effectively inside-out to this because it sees multiplicity in the light of unity instead of trying to produce unity from multiplicity. The important thing to remember here is that, whereas extensively we see many in the form of one (i.e. uniformity), intensively we see One in the form of many. Hence in the intensive perspective each of the many is the very same One, and yet in a way which includes difference instead of eradicating it. This is the difference between a genuinely holistic perspective and the analytical counterfeit. With the distinction between 'unity in multiplicity' and 'multiplicity in unity' it is now possible for us to look at a statement such as "All is leaf" and understand it as an expression

50

of a perception of the universal, and not as an inductive generalization reached empirically by external comparisons and abstraction. In coming to recognize the limitation of Bacon's method, Goethe was feeling his way towards understanding that he was not working with the intellectual mind. He eventually realized that he was working with the intuitive mind, but only after he had first freed himself from the illusion of naive empiricism.[65] We can now understand this precisely in terms of the psychology of consciousness, and we can appreciate why it took Goethe himself some time to begin to clarify the cognitive nature of his own way of science.

At the beginning of this section it was pointed out that Goethe's organic vision has often been misunderstood through failure to realize that he was seeing organic nature in another dimension to space and time. We recognized, in the work on colour, that the unity or wholeness of the phenomenon is an intensive dimension of the phenomenon itself. Now we have developed this further to include organic nature, and have found that organic wholeness is the intensive dimension of One. We can therefore recognize that the other dimension to space and time is this intensive dimension of One, and that the essence of Goethe's organic vision is to see nature in this way. The dimension of One is the intensive depth of the phenomenon when this is organic, and Goethe's notions of the archetypal organ, the archetypal plant, and metamorphosis, all need to be understood in the perspective of this dimension. He saw the plant holistically as One organ, and he saw the entire plant kingdom holistically as One plant. In the language of the hologram metaphor, the many plants are the fragments of a hologram for the archetypal plant, as the plant organs are the fragments of a hologram for the archetypal organ. Metamorphosis is essentially a "multiplication" in the intensive dimension of One, and as such it applies to the plants of the kingdom in the same way as to the organs of the plant. It is therefore an inherently holistic notion which cannot be understood adequately in the analytical mode of consciousness. When the plant kingdom is seen analytically in the extensive perspective of the intellectual mind it appears numerically as the unity in multiplicity of many plants. But if it is seen holistically in the intensive perspective of the intuitive mind it appears non-numerically as the multiplicity in unity of the One plant. The many plants which are one (unity in multiplicity) and the One plant which is many (multiplicity in unity) are really different dimensions of the same individual. Which way it is seen depends on the mode of consciousness.

3.2. The Unity of Animal Organization

Goethe coined the term morphology for the study of form in the plant and

51

animal kingdoms. *Morphe* means 'shape' in Greek, but the form which concerned Goethe was not limited to the external spatial outline of the organism. However, with the tendency to approach the organism through the intellectual mind, the form of the organism as a whole has appeared to be no more than an external aspect of the organism. For this reason, the notion of form has come to be thought of as something which does not refer to an objective feature of the organism in the way that, say, a leg or an eye is an objective feature. Compared with such organs, the form of the organism as a whole seems to be nebulous and unreal. It seems as if it belongs more to the mind of the beholder than to the organism itself. In other words, it seems that believing the 'form of the organism as a whole' to be a real feature of the organism, is a confusion based on mistaking a subjective experience of the observer for an objective aspect of the phenomenon itself. Of course, the form of the organism as a whole cannot be part of the organism in the same way as an individual organ. Nevertheless, Goethe was sure that the form of the organism was something real and not just a figment in the mind of the beholder. He described the task of morphology as being to recognize living forms *as such*, and "to master them, to a certain extent, in their *wholeness* through a concrete vision".[66] The German term which is translated here as 'concrete vision' is *Anschauung*. Agnes Arber, who spent her long life studying plants, said that in this context it "may be held to signify the *intuitive knowledge gained through contemplation of the visible aspect*".[67] This indicates very clearly that Goethe's approach to animal form follows the same pathway that we have discovered in his work on colour. The method, as described above, is active looking followed by exact sensorial imagination, plunging into the visible aspect to produce dishabituation from the verbal-intellectual mind and the analytical mode of consciousness. This exercise of redirecting attention into seeing, inwardly as well as outwardly, therefore removes an obstacle to the holistic mode of consciousness. At the same time, the exercise of trying to see the visible aspect as a whole promotes the re-structuring of consciousness into the holistic mode. This procedure therefore has the result of taking the *Naturschauer* into the phenomenon intuitively and not just sensorially, whilst escaping from the prison of abstractions which is the intellectual mind.[68]

It seems clear from this that the concrete quality which Goethe meant by the form of the organism as a whole can only be perceived adequately in the holistic mode of consciousness. This quality of the wholeness of the organism is another dimension of the organism itself. Goethe's morphology is therefore another example of a way of science which aims to make the phenomenon visible, whereby the *same* phenomenon is seen in another dimension.

The reason for doubting the objective reality of form now becomes apparent. The intellectual mind functions in the analytical mode of consciousness, and it is in the nature of this mode for the organism to be seen as a conglomerate of individual parts. Hence for this mode of consciousness the form of the organism as a whole can only be interpreted as at best a mental abstraction or construction. The concrete experience of living form *as such*, the experience of the wholeness of the organism as a real quality, is only possible in the holistic mode of consciousness. To do morphology in Goethe's sense, therefore, means working with the mind in a different way from the mainstream of science today, which is dominated by the analytical power of the intellectual mind. This is why Goethe's approach to morphology has often not been understood.

The experience of form in Goethe's way leads to an understanding of organisms which differs from seeing them in the light of either finality and purpose or causality and mechanism. It was through the experience of form in the plant kingdom that Goethe came to the understanding of the plant which has been described above. He described his approach to animal form in a conversation with Eckermann, indicating how it differed from the way of understanding which was common at the time:

"Man is inclined to carry his usual views from life also into science and, in observing the various parts of an organic being, to inquire after their purpose and use. This may go on for a while and he may also make progress in science for the time being, but he will come across phenomena soon enough where such a narrow view will prove insufficient and he will be entangled in nothing but contradictions if he does not acquire a higher orientation. Such utilitarian teachers will say that the bull has horns to defend itself with, but there I ask why the sheep has none. Even when they have horns, why are they twisted round the sheep's ears so that they cannot be any use at all? It is a different thing to say that the bull defends himself with his horns because they are there. The question *why* is not scientific at all. We fare a little better with the question *how*, for if I ask the question, 'How does the bull have horns?' I am immediately led to the observation of his organization, and this shows me at the same time why the lion has no horns and cannot have any."[69]

Of course, if Goethe had been writing today he would have addressed his remarks more towards the mechanistic explanation of the animal's appearance. Darwin got rid of "natural purposes", and so he would have agreed with the first part of Goethe's statement. Instead, he explained the features of an organism, such as the giraffe's long neck, by means of "natural selection" acting over long periods of time on small, random variations in the individuals of a breeding population. The overall appearance of a species of organism is thus explained as a long-term statistical effect of the environment acting mechanically on the results of chance. The organism as a whole is not involved, since in Darwin's theory the small random variations are only in individual features of the organism, which are considered separately without any correlation between them. Darwin's organism is a thoroughly analytical organism. Goethe's way of understanding the appearance of an organism in terms of its organization is therefore different from the modern mechanistic explanation, as it was in his own day different from the purposive interpretation.

Goethe himself was only able to go so far with his approach to animal form. For example, he noticed that no animal had a complete set of teeth in its upper jaw if it had horns or antlers. Seeing this connection is an example of *significant* perception, i.e. a perception of meaning, and not just a sensory perception as it seems to the naive empiricist.[70] It was this correlation that enabled Goethe to understand "why the lion has no horns and cannot have any". The fact that he could say the lion *cannot* have horns because it has a complete set of teeth in its upper jaw, means that this connection is perceived to have a quality of *necessity* — this will be discussed in more detail in section 3.2.1. But there were many questions which Goethe could only touch on and not answer fully in terms of the organization of the organism itself. In the above illustration, for example, he was not able to answer why it is precisely the incisors which are missing from the upper jaws of animals with horns or antlers, and why the upper canines are missing as well from the jaws of rhinoceroses and cattle. Such details will inevitably seem very specialized, and perhaps even trivial. But in the holistic biology of animal form each feature of an animal is significant in the context of all the other features, and the whole form of each type of animal is significant in the context of all the other animal types. Thus, questions about horns and antlers can only be answered by taking into account all the mammals, those that do not have these organs as well as those that do. But ultimately this requires a holistic biology of form which takes into account *all* the features of the animal in question, not just horns and teeth, and perceives intuitively the way that they *belong* together in a natural unity without unification.

The glimpse which Goethe had of this holistic biology of animal form has now been turned into a much fuller view by contemporary natural philosophers who are following his way. The most thorough work of this kind has been done on the mammals by Wolfgang Schad.[71] It is described in detail in his book *Man and Mammals*, which it would be difficult to praise too highly for its demonstration of what can be done by following Goethe's way of science far beyond the point that Goethe himself was able to reach. It also has the advantage of a clarity of exposition which makes it available to anyone who is interested. Schad begins from the recognition that there are three fundamental functional processes, or dynamical organic systems, in the mammalian organism. He designates these the nerve-sense system, the respiratory-circulatory system, and the metabolic-limb system. These three dynamical systems are balanced in man, in the sense that no one of them predominates over the others through being more specialized. Although each system is centred in a particular region of the organism, they should not be thought of as being separate and external to each other, lying side-by-side, but as acting simultaneously within each other throughout the whole organism. In other words, they have to be understood holistically and not analytically, as well as dynamically and not statically. They are three processes which act throughout the entire organism, and not localized anatomical features. For example, whereas the nerve-sense system is centred in the head region, there are some features in this region which have the *quality* of the respiratory-circulatory system (the air-filled cavities in the cranium), and also some features which have the *quality* of the metabolic-limb system (the mouth region). But this relationship whereby the whole threefold functional process re-enters each of its own parts — so that the whole is present in its own parts — should not be thought of in a causal-mechanical way. It is not as if the respiratory-circulatory system somehow acted physically in the head region to produce a material modification, and so on. Seeing in the holistic perspective is more a matter of learning to read qualities.

In all the mammals other than man these three functional processes occur in a one-sided way which emphasizes one of them over the other two. The difference between the three major groups of mammals — rodents, carnivores and ungulates — then becomes intelligible in terms of which particular system is dominant.

Thus the rodents (mice, squirrels, rats, beavers, etc.) emphasize the nerve-sense system. This is reflected in the small size of these animals and their restless activity. The trunk and limbs are rudimentary compared with the development of the head, although in many cases the limbs have definitely acquired a sensory function (e.g. the forepaws of a squirrel). The ungulates (horses, pigs, cows, deer, etc.) are the opposite pole to the rodents. These mammals emphasize the metabolic-limb system. This is reflected in the large size of these animals and the elongation of their limbs. Here the metabolic process is so intensified that even the nerve-sense pole of the organism shows the influence of the metabolism in the form of the various head protuberances (horns and antlers). They also exhibit a passive temperament. Finally, the carnivores (cats, weasels, badgers, seals etc.) emphasize the rythmic-circulatory system, which is intermediate between the other two. In their well-proportioned form, in which no one part of the body is accentuated over any other, as well as in their intermediate size, they represent an active balance between the two extremes of the rodent and the ungulate. Their predatory nature fits this intermediate position. A feel for the differences between these groups and the relationships between them can be developed by exact sensorial imagination.

But in any one of these major groups of mammals one of the non-dominant systems can also be accentuated to a lesser degree, and this exerts a secondary influence which modifies the influence of the dominant system. It always has to be remembered that the activities of these systems should be thought of as interpenetrating qualities and not as causal mechanisms. In other words, they should not be thought of in terms which are more appropriate for the world of inorganic bodies. Thus, for example, the squirrel is a rodent. In this case the nerve-sense process dominates the other two, but there is a secondary influence from the respiratory-circulatory process which is absent in the case of other rodents like mice and rats. The beaver, on the other hand, is a rodent with the metabolic-limb process exerting a secondary influence on the nerve-sense process. Similarly, among the ungulates, where the metabolic-limb process is dominant, the horse is an animal which is secondarily influenced by the nerve-sense process, whereas the pig is secondarily influenced by the respiratory-circulatory process.

As well as considering specific mammals, it is also possible to distinguish different groups of mammals, each of which is differentiated within itself as a group according to the same threefoldness that is found in the individual. For example, the swine group as a whole is dominated by the metabolic-limb process and has a secondary influence from the respiratory-circulatory process. The pig is the characteristic member of this group because, as mentioned above, it has exactly this pattern of functional processes. But within *the swine group as a whole* there are other mammals which, while they have this pattern of processes, are also further influenced by either the metabolic-limb process or the nerve-sense process. The former is the case with the hippopotamus, and the latter with the peccary — a slender, belligerent pig from South America. This can be seen more easily by referring to the diagram below. Similarly, in the same group as the horse (the odd-toed ungulates) we find the tapir which is influenced by the respiratory-circulatory process, and the rhinoceros which is influenced by the metabolic-limb process — i.e. in a group which as a whole is dominated by the metabolic-limb process with a secondary influence from the nerve-sense process. Again, the squirrels form a group as a whole which is dominated by the nerve-sense process

56

and has a secondary influence from the respiratory-circulatory process. The squirrel itself is the characteristic member of this group because, as mentioned above, it has just this pattern of functional processes. But within this group *considered as a whole*, the beaver is the mammal which is further influenced by the metabolic-limb process, and the dormouse is the mammal further influenced by the nerve-sense process — and this mammal in turn is further differentiated into different species according to the same threefold structure of functional processes.

The relationships between the few mammals which have been mentioned here for the purpose of illustration can be represented in a diagram. The convention which is adopted is that arrows pointing to the right indicate the influence of the metabolic-limb process; arrows pointing to the left indicate the influence of the nerve-sense process; and arrows which are vertical indicate the influence of the respiratory-circulatory process.[72]

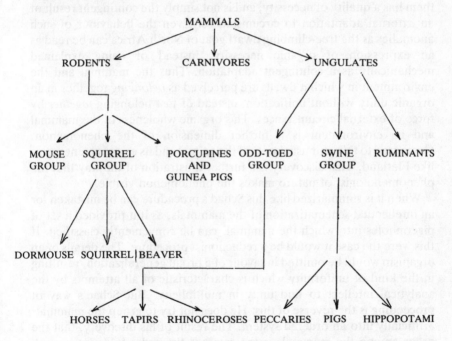

In this kind of way Schad is able to show how the threefold organization of the mammal gives rise to the entire spectrum of the mammalian form — although it is simply not possible to give any idea here of the degree of detail which he goes into with each particular mammal. He shows how the whole form of any particular mammal — including shape, size and colouration — can be understood in terms of the animal's overall organization, so that the animal becomes intelligible in terms of itself. The same threefold organization which is found in any particular mammal is then found to be present in the various groups of mammals, as well as in the mammal family as a whole. Thus the organization of the mammals *as a whole* is understood in terms of the same organization as the individual mammal, so that the individual can then be seen as a reflection of the whole in the part. In this way Schad's holistic biology of form illustrates and extends Goethe's comment to Eckermann that he understands a particular feature of an organism by looking at the overall organization of the animal. Schad then goes even further, and shows in detail how the environment which a particular mammal lives in also reflects the functional process which is predominant within its own organism.[73] There is therefore a truly organic relationship between a mammal and the landscape in which it dwells. The connection between them has a quality of necessity, and is not simply the contingent result of an external adaptation to circumstances. Even the behaviour of such anomalies as the tree-climbing dwarf goat of North Africa can be read as an expression of organic necessity, instead of being explained mechanically as a contingent adaptation. Thus the mammal and the environment in which it dwells are perceived as *belonging* together in an organic unity without unification, instead of just belonging *together* by force of external circumstances. This organic wholeness of the mammal and its environment is a further dimension of the phenomenon. Compared to this, our usual view of the animal and its environment seems like Flatland. This discovery is a further illustration of the way that the phenomenologist of nature makes the phenomenon visible.

When it is summarized like this Schad's procedure can be mistaken for an intellectual schematization of the mammals, as if it provided a set of pigeonholes into which the mammals can be conveniently classified. If this were the case it would be a reductionist procedure. The details of an organism would be omitted in favour of a broad generalization, resulting in the kind of uniformity which is characteristic of all attempts by the analytical intellect to find unity in multiplicity. But Schad's way of proceeding is the reverse of this. He does not try to group the mammals artificially into an ordered system. The result of his discovery, that the order among the mammals is the same as the order inherent in each mammal, is that Schad sees the mammals in the non-reductionist perspective of multiplicity in unity instead of unity in multiplicity. In other words, he sees the mammals in the light of Goethe's organic vision, which permits diversity within the unity and therefore "in no way contradicts the abundant variety of nature".[74] As each detail is significant because it is an expression of an organism's overall organization, so for this very reason every difference between organisms is significant. Thus on the one hand Goethe's organic vision enables difference and uniqueness to be included without falling into sheer multiplicity, while on the other hand it avoids the lifeless unity of uniformity. The difference here is between the perception of multiplicity in an holistic perspective (multiplicity in unity) and the perception of unity in an analytical perspective (unity in multiplicity). It is in the nature of the latter to exclude diversity, whereas it is the nature of the former to include diversity without fragmentation into unrelated multiplicity. Flexibility is the strength of multiplicity in unity, as uniformity is the weakness of unity in multiplicity.

It is through this holistic perspective of multiplicity in unity that Schad is able to understand the organism in terms of itself, so that it becomes its own explanation. His work is therefore a vivid contemporary illustration of what Goethe meant when he said that "the greatest achievement would be to understand that everything factual is already its own theory", and "don't look for anything behind the phenomena; they themselves are the theory". We have seen already (in section 2.3.4) that Goethe's phenomenology is equivalent to what could be called the hermeneutics of nature. The aim of this natural hermeneutics is to learn to read the phenomenon in terms of itself. The holistic biology of animal form illustrates this clearly. When the mammal is disclosed in terms of itself then it becomes its own language. In this moment of intuitive perception the mammal *is* language. This therefore provides us with another concrete instance of Gadamer's principle of universal hermeneutics that "Being that can be understood is language".[75]

3.2.1. The Necessary Connection

It was mentioned briefly in section 2.3.3. that a *relationship* cannot be experienced *as such* in the analytical mode of consciousness. Since in this mode it is the elements which are related that stand out in experience, the relationship itself can only seem to be a shadowy abstraction to the intellectual mind. The perception of a relationship as such would require a simultaneous perception of the whole, and hence the re-structuring of consciousness into the holistic mode. It has been mentioned several times in the discussion of animal form that the phenomenologist of nature perceives connections which have the quality of necessity. Goethe's recognition that an animal with a full set of teeth in its upper jaw *cannot* have horns is an illustration. The perception of a necessary connection *is* the perception of a relationship as a real factor in the phenomenon, instead of being only a mental abstraction added on to what is experienced with the senses. The reality of a relationship, the necessity of a connection, is not experienced as such either by the senses alone or by the intellectual mind. Hence any attempt to understand this reality in terms of these faculties is bound to find that it vanishes from the phenomenon itself and appears to be only a subjective belief.[76]

Schad's work abounds with examples of what he calls "the awesome inner logic of the organism".[77] For example, he describes how the basic tripartite structure of the teeth (incisors, canines and molars) is a reflection of the threefoldness of the functional processes. Hence he shows, in terms of the animal's organization, why the rodents accentuate the incisors, the carnivores accentuate the canines, and the ungulates accentuate the molars. There is therefore a necessary connection between the predominant functional process in an organism and the structure of its teeth — and this extends also to the secondary influence from one of the other functional processes, and so on, in great detail. Here Schad is able to go further than Goethe and understand in terms of the animal's organization why it is precisely the upper incisors which are missing from animals with horns. But he goes even further than this. He shows how the different layers of skin also reflect the three fundamental functional processes, and this enables him to go on to discover the "inner logic" of the specific forms taken by the various kinds of head appendages. So, for example, he is able to understand in terms of the animal's organization why the rhinoceros grows a horn on its snout (and why the canines are missing in its upper jaw as well as the incisors), why the swine grow warts in the middle of the face along their cheeks, and why ruminants grow horns from the rear part of the frontal bone near the back of the head. He subsequently goes on to understand the difference between horns and antlers, showing that, far from being random, the otherwise bewildering variety of antlers can become comprehensible when related to the overall organization of each of the different kinds of deer. What this means is that the existence of each of these different kinds of head appendage is not a contingent fact — as it is usually supposed in "Flatland biology". They are not accidental developments, but real necessities which cannot be otherwise.

Because every detail in an organism is a reflection of its basic organization, there is an intimate correlation between all the features of a particular mammal. With the ruminant ungulates, such as the cow for example, there is an intimate correlation between the horns and hooves and the specialization of the digestive tract at the anterior end. With rodents, on the other hand, there is an intimate correlation between the tail formation (e.g. squirrel, beaver) and the specialization of the digestive tract at the posterior end. There is therefore a necessary connection between these features. But they are not connected in a causal-mechanical way, like the parts of a watch, or even a more sophisticated device with feedback, etc. They *belong* together organically:

"In life, causes and effects take place simultaneously and complement one another. For this reason the organism always presents itself as a whole. Correlations, not causes or aims, determine the order of the life that forms a single whole, because life exists only as a continuing present. The processes of life, therefore, cannot be understood by either causal or teleological ways of thinking; they must be discovered as an active connection existing necessarily among phenomena in the present."[78]

Furthermore, because Schad sees the mammals in the light of multiplicity in unity, it is inevitable that he finds correlations between mammals in different groups. But he is not constrained to look at these correlations as being accidental, which they would be if the correlated features of the organisms in question had arisen simply as external adaptations to the environment by the mechanism of natural selection. For example, among the carnivores there are some which choose water, either wholly or partially, as a habitat. Looking at these mammals in terms of their organization leads to the discovery of a relationship of form between the mink, the otter, the seals and the whales. It emerges that, what the mink is to the weasels, and the otter is to the martens, so the seals are to the central carnivores (e.g. dogs) and the whales are to the carnivores as a whole. This correlation emerges out of the inner logic of the organisms in question, and hence it is "dictated by internal necessity".[79] So the fact that whales exist, for example, can be seen as an organically necessary expression of the fundamental constitution of the mammal itself. Whereas the usual view today is to see the fact that whales exist simply as a contingency, resulting from a long process of external adaptation of a land mammal to life in the sea. Darwin himself said: "I can see no difficulty in a race of bears being rendered, by natural selection, more and more aquatic in their habits, with larger and larger mouths, till a creature was produced as monstrous as a whale."[80] In other words, the fact that whales exist is considered an accident, in the philosophical sense of the term. This misses the dimension of the animal itself. There are many other examples of correlations between mammals in different groups which help to make visible the quality of necessity in the existence of a particular mammal. But there is no need to go into any further examples here.

The assertion that the phenomenologist of nature can find real necessities, i.e. which are in the phenomena themselves and not simply in the mind of the investigator, will seem strange to anybody who is familiar with the history of modern philosophy. The idea that science could discover necessary connections in the phenomena of nature was discarded by many after David Hume's devastating analysis of the principle of causality.[81] Hume's influence on subsequent philosophy has been enormous, and there are many philosophers today who believe that his denial that there are real necessary connections in phenomena which can be known is essentially correct. He reached this sceptical position as a result of following a thoroughly empiricist approach to knowledge. He insisted that all our ideas are copied from our sense impressions, and that all impressions, and hence all ideas, are atomic — i.e. separate and independent of each other. For every idea in the mind he asked the question "From what impression is this idea derived?" Applying this to the idea of a necessary connection in matters of fact, he asked what we can observe which corresponds to the idea of necessity? He could find no sense impression from which this idea can be derived, and hence concluded that there is no justification for believing that the idea of necessity corresponds to anything real. All that we actually experience, according to Hume, is the constant conjunction of two events, and it is their habitual association in the mind which gives us the feeling of necessity. In other words, the origin of the idea of necessity is psychological, and the belief that the necessity is real is an illusion. All that the scientist can discover are purely contingent correlations between phenomena, which therefore might have been otherwise.

By following Goethe's way of science it is possible to experience what Hume denied to human consciousness when he concluded "that all our distinct perceptions are distinct existences, and that the mind never perceives any real connections among distinct existences."[82] Furthermore, through linking Goethe's way with the discovery of two major modes of consciousness, it is possible to see that Hume's sceptical conclusion is a consequence of an extreme identification with the analytical mode of consciousness. What he really did was to describe what knowledge would be like for a purely analytical mode of consciousness. It has already been suggested that such a consciousness could not experience the reality of relationship, since this would require the experience of wholeness. Hence for the analytical mode of consciousness, a relationship could only appear as an abstraction compared with the elements which it relates. Without the experience of the wholeness of the relationship there cannot be any experience of a *necessary* connection. This step is made by a transition to the holistic mode of consciousness, as a result of which we do have the experience corresponding to the idea of necessity, but as an intuition and not as a sense-impression.

Goethe's science of nature, because it makes this transition from the analytical to the holistic mode of consciousness, is therefore a practical way of developing the experience of necessity. Hence it gives the experience which is needed to see the limitation that is the cause of a major philosophical problem. Hume was right, as far as his account went. But he was unaware of the *mode* of consciousness as a determining factor in experience, and so he did not know that another mode of consciousness was possible in which the very factor that he found to be missing can be experienced. It has been noted already (see note 49) that the condition of the knower cannot realistically be separated from what is known. It is, of course, a consequence of the analytical mode of consciousness itself to separate these two and consider them in isolation. Developments in modern physics, especially in the quantum theory, have helped to bring the possibility of making this kind of separation into question. A more comprehensive approach is needed, in which the content of cognition and the condition of consciousness for that cognition are considered as a whole.[83]

It seems to be an unexpected by-product of Goethe's way of science, when it is allied with the distinction between modes of consciousness, that it gives an insight into some of the long-standing problems of philosophy. This is therefore a means of approaching philosophy by the way of experience instead of the way of argument.[84] It has already been mentioned above how some of the difficulties over Plato's theory of Forms have arisen through approaching this theory exclusively by the way of argument, which functions in the analytical mode of consciousness and therefore in the extensive perspective of unity in multiplicity. Yet another example of this experiential way of approaching philosophy now follows from the above discussion of necessity. As well as giving us an insight into the origin of Hume's problem, it also gives us an insight into Aristotle's view of the nature of scientific knowledge. For Aristotle, one of the conditions for something to count as being known is that what is known must be so of necessity; it is not possible for it to be otherwise. Consequently, scientific knowledge is not knowledge of what happens to be true — since this would not be 'knowledge' for Aristotle — but of what *cannot* be otherwise and hence *must* be true. This really does seem strange to us now that we have been deeply infected by the empirical tradition, whether we are aware of it or not. It seems to us a matter of commonsense that facts are contingent. For example, it seems to be no more than a contingent fact that lions don't have horns — and this is certainly how it seems to biology in the Darwinian paradigm. We can imagine that it could have been otherwise, or that there could be a lion with horns somewhere yet to be discovered. But we have learned from Goethe's approach to animal form, especially as developed by Schad, that there are many facts about the mammals which superficially appear to be contingent and yet turn out to be necessary when perceived with the intuitive mind. Aristotle would have understood exactly what Goethe meant when, in his remark to Eckermann, he asserted that the fact that the lion has no horns *cannot* be otherwise.[85]

Recently there has been a resurgence of interest in Aristotle's philosophy of knowledge. This is partly a consequence of the work of the American philosopher, Saul Kripke, who has argued that there can be necessarily true propositions which describe essential properties of things in the world, and hence which are not merely logically necessary and therefore empty of factual content.[86] Thus he attempts to refute Hume's view that there cannot be propositions which are both necessary and give information about the world. He maintains, for example, that the fact that gold is yellow should not be taken to be contingent, as if the colour yellow were an accident, but that it should be taken to be a necessary property which is true "in all possible worlds". There cannot be blue gold — anymore than there can be a lion with horns, or a cow with a single stomach. So Kripke arrives at the position taken by Aristotle — and by Goethe. But because he belongs to the school of analytical philosophy, which proceeds by the way of argument, his philosophy does not bring us to *experience* necessity in the world. This remains an intellectual abstraction. Goethe's approach to science, through the holistic mode of consciousness, could therefore provide the intuitive experience of necessity which would complement what can be achieved by means of argument.

Clearly, the understanding of the animal as a whole which emerges from Goethe's organic vision is very different to the way that the animal is understood in Darwin's theory of evolution by natural selection. For the organic perspective, the different features of an animal are expressions of the whole animal and not just useful adaptations. But for Darwinism the animal is a contingency. There is no form of the animal as a whole, with necessary connections which result in an intrinsically intelligible structure. Instead, the animal is conceived as a bundle of features which are considered to be effectively separate and independent of each other, because any one of them is capable of varying independently by chance. Whether such a variation is biologically viable is then determined by the environment, and not by any factors which are intrinsic to the organism. This is the analytical organism which is implied by the mechanism of the Darwinian theory. In other words, it is a constraint of the theory that the animal comes to be seen in this way. In place of necessary connection and wholeness, there is simply contiguity and constant conjunction — it is little wonder that the Darwinian animal has been called a Humean bundle.[87]

Darwin approached the animal in the analytical mode of consciousness. So there is no perception of internal relationships in the organism — as with Newton there is no perception of relationships between the colours. Yet there is clear evidence of a more holistic approach to animal form among the breeders Darwin met. In *The Origin of Species* he refers to breeders who "habitually speak of the animal's organization as something quite plastic".[88] He recounts how in one place "the sheep are placed on a table and are studied, like a picture by a connoisseur", and how it had been said of sheep breeders that "it would seem as if they had chalked out upon a wall a perfect form itself, and then had given it existence". It is just this sense of the organism as a whole which disappeared in Darwin's theory, with the result that "the organism as a real entity, existing in its own right, has virtually no place in contemporary biological theory".[89] However, Darwin himself was not quite so dogmatic as his followers became. In focussing only on what had survival value for the individual and the species, he overlooked the purely morphological study of living organisms. Eventually he recognized this limitation in his approach, and said that it was "one of the greatest oversights".[90]

The holistic biology of form shows in abundant detail how misleading the wholesale application of the theory of natural selection can be, because it eclipses those relationships which belong to the organism as a whole. Thus a dimension of the organism is lost, with the result that the organism is interpreted only as it appears in an analytical Flatland. This disappearance of the organism as a whole is even more acute today than it was in Darwin's time, because of the alliance of Darwin's theory with genetics. The development of molecular biology has now taken it a stage further. The result is that the organism has now been replaced by microscopic entities hidden behind the scenes, like the mechanism in Einstein's watch. But now that there is a growing feeling of dissatisfaction with the current evolutionary paradigm, it is beginning to be recognized that an adequate understanding depends on "the reinstatement of the organism as the proper object of biological research; as a real object, existing in its own right and to be explained in its own terms".[91] This is where Goethe began.

4. The Scientist's Knowledge

In conclusion we will look briefly at Goethe's view on the nature of scientific knowledge itself. In doing so we find an understanding of knowledge which is very different from the way that we understand it today — although it would not have been so unfamiliar to Goethe's contemporaries, and especially not to such philosophers as Schelling and Hegel. We consider knowledge to be a subjective state of the knower, a modification of consciousness which in no way affects the phenomenon that is known, this being the same whether it is known or not. Goethe, on the other hand, saw the knowledge of a phenomenon as being intimately related to the phenomenon itself, because for him the state of 'being known' was to be understood as a further stage of the phenomenon itself. It is the stage which the phenomenon reaches in human consciousness. Consequently the knower is not an onlooker but a participant in nature's processes, which now act in consciousness to produce the phenomenon consciously as they act externally to produce it materially. This is the meaning of Goethe's remark that the aim of science should be that "through the contemplation of an ever creating nature, we should make ourselves worthy of spiritual participation in her production".

If 'being known' is a higher stage of the phenomenon itself, then the phenomenon should not be imagined as being complete whether it is known or not. The participatory view of the role of consciousness in knowledge is therefore an evolutionary view, in the widest sense, because the state of 'being known' is an evolutionary development of nature itself. When consciousness is properly prepared it becomes the medium in which the phenomenon itself comes into presence. We call this 'knowing the phenomenon', and understand it subjectively. But in a more comprehensive view it *is* the phenomenon itself which appears in consciousness when it is known. The act of knowing is an evolutionary development of the phenomenon and not just a subjective activity of man. This is the ontological significance of intuitive knowledge. The true significance of 'theory' now becomes apparent. When the phenomenon becomes its own theory, this is a higher stage of the phenomenon itself. Evidently this does not apply to the kind of theory which is an intellectual framework imposed on the phenomenon by the mind — as discussed in section 2.3.2. Thus the phenomenologist of nature himself becomes the apparatus in which the phenomenon actualizes as a higher stage of itself. This brings us to a more comprehensive form of the principle of the wholeness of the apparatus and the phenomenon being investigated (see note 49). In this case the scientist himself becomes the apparatus in which the phenomenon appears. Hence, for the intuitive knowledge of nature, when the phenomenon becomes its own theory, we have the ontological condition that the knower and the known constitute an indivisible whole.

What makes this particularly difficult for us to understand is the extreme separation between subject and object, consciousness and the world, which is characteristic of the onlooker consciousness. This separation is a consequence of over-reliance on the intellectual mind and the analytical mode of consciousness with which it is associated. Although this extreme dependence on the verbal-intellectual mind developed over a period of time throughout western Europe as a whole, it is demonstrated particularly clearly in the writings of Descartes. For this reason he can be taken as representative of the shift in awareness which marks the emergence of modern western man. Although he is famous for his statement "I think, therefore I am", he is best approached through his first two *Meditations*.[92] Here, in a few pages, he shows how he was led to doubt the existential status of his experience. Since he cannot tell whether he is dreaming or not, he cannot be certain that the world exists, or even that his own body exists. He indicates how he eventually came to experience a feeling of certainty that "I am, I exist" in the act of thinking itself. So he is led to identify himself as a thinking being, and as such he feels himself to be separate and independent from the world, as well as from his own body. Descartes then equated thinking with subjective experience in the widest sense — which subsequently came to be identified with consciousness.[93] Thus the famous Cartesian dualism between consciousness and the world was born, and it is inherent in this dualism that consciousness has the role of onlooker to a world which is outside itself.

It is well-known that, as soon as Descartes' philosophy is looked into, it rapidly becomes incoherent — and much of modern philosophy has been concerned with the attempt to break away from the Cartesian framework. For example, Descartes identified the world with the property of extension; hence consciousness *must* be non-extended. But if consciousness is non-spatial, how can the world be 'outside' it? As Gilbert Ryle put it: "What is the External World external to?"[94] Can we even *count* consciousness and world as 'two' without thereby reifying consciousness in our imagination, as if it were a ghostly thing, and thus contradicting its essential nature? Even if we ignore these difficulties, as many have, there remains the problem of how two factors which are divorced so exclusively can ever be related. Thus it becomes a problem as to how unextended mind and extended body can interact. Similarly, it becomes a problem as to how the subject can arrive at knowledge of the external world. But any attempt to solve these problems must be self-defeating, because it rests on the very assumption which generated them in the first place. Heidegger has called the persistence of the question "How does the subject arrive at knowledge of the so-called external world?" the real scandal of philosophy.[95] In fact Hume demonstrated, over two centuries ago, that the attempt to take subjective experience as a starting point ultimately leads to total scepticism about the existence of a self which has that experience. In other words, Hume made the incoherence in Descartes' philosophy fully visible.[96]

Yet the fact remains that this is how we do think of ourselves in relationship to the world. We do have an impression of ourselves as being separate and independent from the world, detached from nature, which puts us in the position of being onlookers. It is this sense of separation that gives us the attitude which is necessary to be able to treat the world as an object to be operated on, manipulated and organized. In other words, this is the condition of consciousness which is necessary for us to approach the world from our modern technological standpoint, both instrumentally and conceptually. It has been pointed out often enough that it is only by withdrawing ourselves from the world that we can feel sufficiently separate to be able to approach it in a detached way as an object. Subject and object are born together, so that a change in the mode of one necessarily entails a change in the mode of the other. It has also been pointed out equally often how this attitude developed strongly in western Europe during the sixteenth and seventeenth centuries. It has been mentioned in section 2.1 how the development of science from Newton to Goethe was in the direction of *measuring* nature, i.e. concerned with those aspects of nature which can be represented quantitatively. In order to do this it is necessary to organize nature with a network of concepts which we impose on nature. The mathematically-based physicist then works with these conceptual representations instead of with the perceived phenomena. We are so accustomed to this that we do not realize just how much the physicist inhabits a thought-world of his own making, and hence we identify this thought-world with nature itself. To recognize this needs a shift of attention to make the activity of the mind visible to itself. The mathematical physicist and the industrial entrepreneur are alike in that they are both concerned with the technical-conceptual organization of what they see as 'the external world'. Both depend on the onlooker condition of consciousness for which it is "commonsense" that knowing is a subjective state of the knower, and the knower is ontologically separate from the known.

This 'onlooker' condition of consciousness is a consequence of emphasizing the thinking activity of the intellectual mind. We can see this quite easily by returning to Descartes. He liked to spend his mornings in bed "meditating" in a thinking kind of way. In this situation his attention was withdrawn from the world, as well as from his own body, and focussed onto the activity of thinking. Thus, whereas his body was inactive, his thinking activity was by comparison hyperactive. The psychological effect of doing this was to produce an awareness of the world and his body as being outside himself, together with the feeling that he himself existed in this intensified activity of his mind. Hence he experienced a strong sense of being separate from the world, and even his body, which therefore seemed unreal compared with his mental activity. Through directing his attention onto the thinking activity of the intellectual mind he became an onlooker-consciousness. He felt himself to be identified with his thinking activity, and he expressed this feeling that *he* existed in thinking by "I think, therefore I am", or by saying "I am, I exist" as a being whose nature is to think and no more. In fact, as mentioned already, he then widened this to include all of what today we would call 'conscious experience'. Thus the Cartesian dualism and the onlooker consciousness are *psychological* consequences of emphasizing the verbal-intellectual activity of the mind. Descartes' philosophy is therefore a projection of the psychological state which he produced in himself. In other words, he made himself into a psychological apparatus for producing the Cartesian philosophy. Once again we find that a more comprehensive approach is needed, in which the content of cognition and the condition of consciousness for that cognition must be considered as a whole. Evidently this is just what the *onlooker* consciousness cannot do. But Descartes' philosophy must be considered even more comprehensively. It is also an expression of an historical-cultural situation, which it simultaneously helped to produce, and not merely the subjective expression of an isolated individual.

It is inevitable that when Goethe's understanding of scientific knowledge is seen through Cartesian spectacles it seems to make knowledge into something entirely subjective. Goethe's view could be called "organic" because it sees knowledge as a further development of the phenomenon itself. In point of fact, a more organic understanding of knowledge preceded the modern period, although this is often missed because of the inevitable tendency to look back towards earlier periods with the perspective of the onlooker consciousness. Owen Barfield, for example, draws a parallel between Goethe and Aristotle. Pointing out that the primal phenomenon of colour and the organic archetypes are neither objective nor subjective, he says:

"They come into existence *as* types, or *as* laws, only as they are intuited by human beings. And until they have so come into being, the object itself is incomplete. Knowledge in fact, so far from being a mental copy of events and processes outside the human being, inserts the human being right *into* these processes, of whose development it is itself the last stage."[97]

He sees this as being parallel to Aristotle's conception in *De Anima* of the reality (*eidos*) which only exists potentially (*dunamei*) until it is known, and when it is known it has its full existence actually (*energeia*). Aristotle's understanding of knowledge was elaborated further by Aquinas in the Middle Ages.[98] But this organic understanding of knowledge, which sees it as a mode of participation in the phenomenon, was not restricted to the Aristotelian tradition. Gadamer reminds us that "this involvement of knowledge in being is the presupposition of all classical and mediaeval thought". So the philosophers of these earlier periods conceived "knowledge as an element of being itself and not primarily as an attitude of the subject".[99] If we look on this "involvement of knowledge in being" as a remnant of primitive animism, this in itself is an indication that we are perceiving it with the Cartesian attitude of the onlooker consciousness.

After the emergence of the onlooker consciousness as the dominant attitude of modern western culture, the perspective of the knower as a participant in the known became an underground minority viewpoint. Whenever it came to the surface, as it did from time to time, it was usually misunderstood because it was interpreted in the perspective of the onlooker consciousness. Goethe's own period in Germany was such a time. The organic understanding of knowledge emerged in the Romantic movement, post-Kantian philosophy, and the philosophical approach to nature (*Naturphilosophie*). It was from his contact with the philosopher Schelling, for example, that Goethe learned how his own way of science exemplified a participatory way of knowing nature. Schelling held the view that in knowing nature the scientist produces nature — which looks like an extreme form of subjective idealism to the onlooker consciousness. It was in the light of what he learned from Schelling that Goethe subsequently expressed the aim of his science to be that "through the contemplation of an ever creating nature, we should make ourselves worthy of spiritual participation in her production".[100] As the waves of influence from these movements spread outwards in space and time they inevitably became more diluted, eventually degenerating into romanticism and sentimentality.[101] It is surprising to discover how widespread the influence of the organic understanding of scientific knowledge was — even if it was sometimes only sentimental. For example, we find the man we usually think of as a hard-headed Victorian materialist, T.H. Huxley, contributing Goethe's prose aphorisms on Nature as the opening article for the first number of the weekly science journal *Nature*. Huxley commented: "It seemed to me that no more fitting preface could be put before a journal, which aims to mirror the progress of that fashioning by Nature of a picture of herself, in the mind of man, which we call the progress of science."[102]

As stated in the Introduction, the real value of Goethe's way of science is independent of any comparison, favourable or otherwise, with the mainstream of science. Also, the value of Goethe's way is not to be found in whatever individual discoveries he may have made. The real value of his original approach to science is that it is a new way of doing science, and a new way of seeing Nature as a whole. As such it belongs to the present and not to the past. It is an original event of perception in which we can learn to participate. By seeing how the philosophy of Goethe's way of science is illuminated by contemporary European philosophy, and especially how the psychology of this science is clarified by recent research into the psychology of consciousness, we can begin to recognize that this is an authentic way of science in its own right. The science which belongs to the intuitive mind and the holistic mode of consciousness can reveal aspects of the phenomena of nature which *must* be invisible to the verbal-intellectual mind and the analytical mode of consciousness. No matter how sophisticated today's institutionalized science may become, or how much further it may be developed, it will still be concerned predominantly with only the quantitative aspects of phenomena, which can be measured and represented by a number. No matter how beautiful, elegant and harmonious the equations may be to the mathematical physicist, the fact remains that the variables in the equations represent quantities. Hence science today is concerned with only one aspect of the phenomena, and there are other aspects which cannot be reached in this way. Goethe's way of science, by contrast, can be seen as the science of quality instead of quantity — but we need to have the corresponding experience to understand what this means.[103]

At a time when, once again, some physicists are saying that the key to the Universe is in sight, it may be useful to be reminded that the science in which they work is only one-dimensional, and that there are aspects of the phenomena to which it is blind. To be able to see these other aspects there would need to be a transformation of science itself. But this needs a transformation of the scientist. The result of such a transformation would be a radical change in our awareness of the relationship between Nature and ourselves. Instead of mastery over Nature, the scientist's knowledge would become the synergy of man and Nature. The historical value of Goethe's work, in the wider sense, may be that he provides us with an instance of how this can be done. If this should turn out to be the historical significance of Goethe, then our present science will be only a phase in the development of science. Goethe will then be seen as a precursor of a whole new way of science, for which, to paraphrase Goethe himself, he will be "an instance worth a thousand, bearing all within himself".

72

Notes and References

1. Rudolf Magnus, *Goethe as a Scientist* (New York: Collier Books, 1961), p.22.
2. English-speaking historians often refer to this as the Whig interpretation of history, using a particular instance to designate a general historical outlook. See Hugh Kearney, *Science and Change 1500-1700* (London: Weidenfeld and Nicholson, 1971), pp. 17-22.
3. Rudolf Steiner, *Goethe the Scientist* (New York: Anthroposophic Press, 1950), p.15 and p.31.
4. Ted Bastin (ed.) *Quantum Theory and Beyond* (Cambridge: Cambridge University Press, 1971), pp. 321-34.
5. Rudolf Steiner, op. cit. p.1.
6. Norwood Russell Hanson, *Patterns of Discovery* (Cambridge: Cambridge University Press, 1958), p.13.
7. Ernst Lehrs, *Man or Matter* (London: Rudolf Steiner Press, Third Edition, Revised and Enlarged, 1985), p.131.
8. Isaac Newton, "The Origin of Colours," in Michael Roberts and E.R. Thomas, *Newton and the Origin of Colours* (London: Bell, 1934), pp. 71-91.
9. Isaac Newton, *Opticks* (New York: Dover, 1952), p.124.
10. For example, a science report in *The Times* (London, December 4, 1984, p.16), begins: "In much the way that beams of ordinary light comprise a mixture of colours of the rainbow,...."
11. A much more detailed treatment is given in Lehrs, op. cit.
12. The spectrum described by Newton, and repeated in physics books, contains seven colours: red, orange, yellow, green, blue, indigo and violet. But most observers find they can only distinguish six colours- indigo is missing. Newton's choice of seven colours has been traced to his interest in musical theory, and the Pythagorean division of the octave into seven intervals. See I. Bernard Cohen, *The Newtonian Revolution* (Cambridge: Cambridge University Press, 1980), p.205.
13. Idries Shah, *A Perfumed Scorpion* (London: Octagon Press, 1978), p.25.
14. Norwood Russell Hanson, *Perception and Discovery* (San Francisco: Freeman, 1969), p.61.
15. Designed by Jackie Bortoft.
16. See note 6.
17. Ludwig Wittgenstein, *Philosophical Investigations* (Oxford: Blackwell, 1968), p.169.
18. The view that the proper objects of perception are meanings has been presented with considerable clarity and cogency by the the philosopher of

science, Harold. I. Brown, in *Perception, Theory and Commitment* (Chicago: University of Chicago Press, 1977), chapter 6.

19. Merleau-Ponty, for example, considers the case of someone whose perception is abnormal, because of an injury, as a means of understanding normal perception. This is discussed in detail in M. Merleau-Ponty, *Phenomenology of Perception* (London: Routledge and Kegan Paul, 1962). Because the proper objects of perception are meanings, Merleau-Ponty is led to say: "Because we are in the world, we are *condemned to meaning" (p.xix)* — which expresses dramatically in the language of existentialism what has now been said more soberly in the philosophy of science. Other cases are provided by the experience of persons who, having been blind from birth because of cataracts, eventually receive their sight as a result of an operation. Their experiences are described in M. von Senden, *Space and Sight* (London: 1960). A particularly clear discussion of the state of purely sensory experience is given by Rudolf Steiner in *A Theory of Knowledge Based on Goethe's World Conception* (New York: Anthroposophic Press, 1968), chapter 5.

20. A fairly straightforward account of Husserl's phenomenology is given in David Stuart and Algis Mickunas, *Exploring Phenomenology* (Chicago: American Library Association, 1974), chapters 1 and 2. See also the introductory essay by Peter Koestenbaum in Edmund Husserl, *The Paris Lectures* (The Hague: Martinus Nijhoff, 1975).

21. The notion of intentionality was introduced by Husserl's teacher, Franz Brentano, who incorporated it into modern philosophy from the pre-Cartesian philosophy of the Middle Ages.

22. Galileo described his observations in *Siderius Nuncius (The Starry Messenger)*, which is included in Stillman Drake, *Discourses and Opinions of Galileo* (New York: Doubleday, 1957). See also the discussion in I. Bernard Cohen, op. cit. (note 12), section 4.7.

23. The priority of meaning in scientific discovery is shown clearly by Bernard Cohen's discovery that the celebrated Newtonian synthesis was not a synthesis of elements which already existed beforehand. They did not fly together like fragments in a reversed explosion, in the way that Koestler maintained in *The Sleepwalkers* (Harmondsworth: Penguin Books, 1964, p.517), because the elements were transformed in their meaning in the so-called "synthesis". Newton's discovery is a whole way of seeing and as such it influenced all the elements which it incorporated. An original perception of meaning transforms the meaning of the individual elements which it uses, so that they reflect the new meaning. Cohen has researched this transformation of ideas in detail in *The Newtonian Revolution*, op. cit.

Recognition of the priority of meaning in scientific discovery was made earlier by Paul Feyerabend in his essay "Explanation, Reduction and Empiricism", which is now republished in Paul K. Feyerabend, *Realism, Rationalism and Scientific Method* (Cambridge: Cambridge University Press, 1981). He realized that meaning is not an invariant in scientific knowledge, and that there are no 'established facts' because a fact can be altered by a change of meaning. The facts of science are inherently mutable. This is not because there are more yet to be discovered, but because the facts which have been discovered already can change in themselves. This is illustrated beautifully by Galileo's discovery that a body is indifferent to its state of motion. He did not discover this empirically, as if it were a fact which hitherto had been overlooked. The discovery was a change of the meaning in the facts of motion, which transformed these facts themselves so that they became coherent with a Copernican Universe instead of with an Aristotelian one. To take a cinematographical analogy, we can change what is on the screen by changing the film in the projector, but somebody who was unfamiliar with the cinema — an "empiricist" — might think that the change had happened on the screen. Galileo's cognitive procedure is also discussed by Paul Feyerabend in *Against Method* (London: Verso, 1978) in a way which illustrates the priority of meaning in scientific knowledge — although Feyerabend uses this valuable study to support his own colourful interpretation of science in terms of an anarchistic epistemology.

Thomas Kuhn's seminal essay, *The Structure of Scientific Revolutions* (Chicago: University of Chicago Press, second edition 1970), can also be seen retrospectively as disclosing the priority of meaning in science. See, for example, his discussion in chapter six of the difference between Priestley and Lavoisier over the discovery of oxygen. Here again is a study which shows that there are no 'established facts' in the way the empiricist imagines, and that what the facts are depends on the perception of meaning.

In view of these developments in the contemporary philosophy of science, it now seems somewhat strange that the priority of meaning in scientific discovery was not recognized explicity for so long. It seems as if the meaning of 'meaning' was not recognized. This could simply be because philosophers of science have traditionally worked in a different philosophical paradigm from one in which 'meaning' was itself recognized as a primary element of experience.

24. Phenomenalism is described in R. Harré, *The Philosophies of Science* (Oxford: Oxford University Press, 1972). Positivism, in all its various forms, is discussed in Leszek Kolakowski, *Positivist Philosophy* (Harmondsworth: Penguin Books, 1972).

25. The impact of positivism on science education is clearly reflected in the text books. A typical example is provided by a well-known textbook in physics: Gerald Holton and Duane H.D. Roller, *Foundations of Modern Physical Science* (Reading, Mass.: Addison-Wesley, 1958), especially chapter 13.

26. Martin Heidegger, *Identity and Difference* (New York: Harper and Row, 1969), p.29.

27. Robert E. Ornstein, *The Psychology of Consciousness* (New York: Harcourt Brace Jovanovich, 1977).

28. Henri Bergson, *Creative Evolution* (London: Macmillan, 1969), p.169.

29. For example in Benjamin Lee Whorf, *Language, Thought, and Reality* (Cambridge, Mass.: M.I.T. Press, 1964). Also in David Bohm, *Wholeness and the Implicate Order* (London: Routledge and Kegan Paul, 1980), chapter 2.

30. It is because of this transparency of language that we think the function of language is representational — to represent what is already present — whereas the primary function of language is to disclose. Language, in this fundamental

sense, *is* the event of the appearance of what becomes present — 'appearance' is used here in the verbal sense of 'coming forth into view'. This disclosive function of language is encapsulated in the well-known question: "How do I know what I think until I see what I say?" The commonsense view of language misses this, and imagines instead that language is simply a tool which is applied to what we *already* know (i.e. in advance of language) for the purpose of communication. The difference between the representational and the disclosive functions of language is fundamental to the modern philosophy of language, especially as it has been developed by Hans-Georg Gadamer out of the work of Martin Heidegger. A lucid general introduction is given in Richard E. Palmer, *Hermeneutics* (Evanston: Northwestern University Press, 1969). The way in which language itself disappears in its living operation is discussed in Hans-Georg Gadamer, *Philosophical Hermeneutics* (Berkeley: University of California Press, 1976), p.64 et seq.

It should be noted that Whorf's account, referred to in note 29, is in one way too analytical itself. He refers, for example, to dissecting nature, cutting it up, and organizing it along lines laid down by our native language (p.213). This presupposes that the primary function of language is instrumental, i.e. that language is imposed externally on a pre-existing world. Although this is an advance on the naivety of commonsense, which reduces language to a triviality, it nevertheless leads to a form of subjectivism which is ultimately a cul-de-sac. It is this cul-de-sac which the modern philosophy of language aims to avoid.

31. David Bohm, op. cit. note 29. Also, David Bohm, *Quantum Theory* (New Jersey: Prentice-Hall, 1951), chapter 8. The problem of wholeness in quantum physics is also considered in connection with the structure of language in P.H. Bortoft, *A Non-reductionist Perspective for the Quantum Theory*, M. Phil. thesis, London University, 1982.

32. Robert E. Ornstein, *The Mind Field* (London: Octagon Press, 1983), chapters 2 and 3.

33. The discovery was made early on in Greek philosophy that motion and change appear as something paradoxical when the attempt is made to understand the world through the rational mind. Although they were not originally intended for the purpose, Zeno's famous paradoxes of motion can be taken as indicating the kind of self-contradiction we get into if we try to grasp motion by rational thought, i.e. with the analytical approach of the intellectual mind. In the paradox of the flying arrow, for example, it seems that the arrow must be stationary at any instant of its flight, because at any instant it must be at a definite location, and hence the moving arrow cannot be moving because it is everywhere instantaneously at rest. Thus the attempt to analyse motion has the effect of stopping motion and reconstituting it in the mind as a succession of states of rest. The inherent absurdity of this procedure, whereby motion is produced out of rest, as if it were some kind of optical illusion, has been discussed very fully in more recent philosophy by Henri Bergson in *Creative Evolution* (op. cit., note 28) and other works. He recognized that this reflected an intrinsic limitation of the rational mind itself, and he considered the possibility of a transformation of the mind into an intuitive mode whereby the reality of *change* itself can be

experienced directly. What this amounts to is a transformation in the mode of consciousness — it will be mentioned subsequently that, whereas the analytical mode is the mode of consciousness for the intellectual mind, the mode of consciousness corresponding to the intuitive mind is the holistic mode.

The peculiar difficulty which motion and change present to the understanding was considered very thoroughly in antiquity by Aristotle. The foundation of his physics was the reality of change as a *mode of being*. Etienne Gilson said that "No one has ever better discerned the mystery that the very familiarity of movement hides from our eyes" — *The Spirit of Mediaeval Philosophy* (London: Sheed and Ward, 1950), p.66. But Aristotle's philosophy of change often seems to be enigmatic. His statement that "change is the actuality of the potential *qua* such" (*Physics*, book III) seems particularly obscure. It is usually possible to perform an intellectual sleight of hand on Aristotle's philosophy of change, and present it as being either platitudinous or just good common sense. But these intellectual reductions miss the point. For example, the statement above is not a definition of change, as is often supposed, but the expression of an insight into the reality of change as a way of being. The intellectual mind itself cannot grasp this because of the analytical mode of consciousness. It may be the case that Aristotle's philosophy of change can only be appreciated adequately in the holistic mode of consciousness, when it will be seen that, far from being just good common sense, Aristotle is trying to indicate something extraordinary. In other words, the so-called obscurity in Aristotle's philosophy of change may be a consequence of the mode of consciousness in which we try to understand it, in which case the difficulty could be removed by extending our experience instead of relying on verbal arguments.

It is also worth noticing that the perception of motion and change in the holistic mode of consciousness leads to a new understanding of causality. In the state of dynamical simultaneity, cause and effect are simultaneous. But in the analytical mode of consciousness, cause and effect are considered sequentially in a linear way : the cause precedes its effect, as the effect follows the cause. This will be discussed further in section 3.2.1. below, where David Hume's investigation of causality in terms of juxtaposition and succession will be examined in the light of the difference between analytical and holistic modes of consciousness. For the moment we will simply note that what Goethe said about causality fits in very well with dynamical simultaneity and the holistic mode of consciousness: "Who strives after cause and effect makes a great mistake. They are together the indivisible phenomenon."

34. Arthur J. Deikman, "Bimodal Consciousness" and "Deautomatization and the Mystic Experience" in Robert E. Ornstein, (ed.), *The Nature of Human Consciousness*, (San Francisco: Freeman, 1973).

35. Arthur J. Deikman, "Bimodal Consciousness", p.76.

36. Robert E. Ornstein, *The Mind Field*, p.52 et seq.

37. Robert E. Ornstein, *The Psychology of Consciousness*, p.184.

38. Robert E. Ornstein, *The Mind Field*, p.24.

39. Ibid., p.26.

40. It is interesting in this connection that Goethe described himself as a

Naturschauer (nature looker) instead of the more usual *Naturforscher* (nature investigator).

41. Niels Bohr, *Atomic Theory and the Description of Nature* (Cambridge: Cambridge University Press, 1961).

42. Albert Einstein and Leopold Infeld, *The Evolution of Physics* (Cambridge: Cambridge University Press, 1947), p.33.

43. Norwood Russell Hanson, *Patterns of Discovery*, chapter 1.

44. See R.G. Collingwood, *The Idea of Nature* (Oxford: Oxford University Press, 1960), p.126.

45. This will be discussed further in section 4 below.

46. Martin Heidegger, *Being and Time* (London: SCM Press, 1962), pp. 51,58.

47. Hans-Georg Gadamer, *Truth and Method* (London: Sheed and Ward, 1979), p.432.

48. A.G.F. Gode von Aesch, *Natural Science in German Romanticism* (New York: Columbia University German Studies, 1941), p. 74.

49. Rudolf Steiner, *The Philosophy of Freedom* (London: Rudolf Steiner Press, 1964), especially chapter 7. Philosophically, this leads to a non-reductionist monism in which many of the traditional problems associated with the philosophy of knowledge simply do not arise. It is interesting that modern physics has made a significant step towards this viewpoint, but it has not yet gone as far as Steiner. Thus, in the quantum theory, Niels Bohr proposed the new fundamental principle that the physical system being investigated by an experiment could not be separated from the apparatus being used to investigate it. He proposed that, because of the indivisibility of the quantum, the system and the apparatus constitute an indivisible whole and must be considered as such. David Bohm suggested that this should be extended to include the theory as well, since the apparatus in question is a concrete expression of the theory. We shall see in sections 3.2.1. and 4 below how Bohr's principle needs to be extended further still to include the state of consciousness of the knowing observer, so that it now becomes the wholeness of the content of cognition and the condition of consciousness for that cognition. Each of these steps represents a movement away from the subject-object dualism, which selects only a portion of the whole for attention, and imagines that the other portion is merely a spectator. This movement towards a more comprehensive viewpoint was taken further still by Steiner. He considered man to be part of the total situation by virtue of his organization as a human being. Far from being merely a spectator who looks on, man is now understood to be an integral factor within the process of cognition, which is seen to be a non-subjective expression of the process of actualization of the universe at a higher stage than the material level. This will be discussed briefly in connection with Goethe in section 4 below.

50. Edwin A. Abbott, *Flatland* (New York: Dover, 1952).

51. J.W. von Goethe, *The Metamorphosis of Plants* (Wyoming: Biodynamic Literature, 1978), p.20. This essay is also available in Agnes Arber, *Chronica Botanica*, vol. 10, 1946.

52. Ibid.

53. Ernst Cassirer, *The Problem of Knowledge* (New Haven: Yale University

Press, 1974), p.145.

54. Rudolf Magnus, op. cit., p.45.
55. Henri Bortoft, "Counterfeit and Authentic Wholes" in David Seamon and Robert Mugerauer (eds.), *Dwelling, Place and Environment: Essays Toward a Phenomenology of Person and World* (The Hague: Martinus Nijhoff, 1986).
56. Gerbert Grohmann, *The Plant* (London: Rudolf Steiner Press, 1974), p.43.
57. For an account of how metamorphosis can be described in terms of Bohm's distinction between implicate and explicate orders, see P.H. Bortoft, op. cit. note 31.
58. The role of imagination in this context is referred to in Seyyed Hossein Nasr, *Science and Civilization in Islam* (Cambridge, Mass.: Harvard University Press, 1968), p. 257. See also Ernst Lehrs, op. cit., for a discussion of the faculty of imagination as an organ or perception. See also Elémire Zolla, *The Uses of Imagination and the Decline of the West* (Ipswich: Golgonooza Press, 1978), p.29.
59. Agnes Arber, *The Natural Philosophy of Plant Form* (Cambridge: Cambridge University Press, 1959), p. 209. Arber is quoting Wilhelm Troll, Professor of Botany at the University of Mainz, who developed a new plant typology working from Goethean foundations earlier this century. A picture of Turpin's ideal plant is given in Jochen Bockemühl, *In Partnership with Nature* (Wyoming: Bio-Dynamic Literature, 1981), p.4.
60. The dictionary gives the meaning of 'intensive' in terms of intensity, but the meaning in mathematics (which comes from medieval philosophy) is not the same as this. It can be illustrated most easily by way of examples. In logic, for example, "the king is dead" and "le roi est mort" are two different statements but a single proposition. The proposition is the intension of the statements, and the statements are the extensions of the proposition. The mathematical notion of a set is closely related to this. For example, a set of tables is defined by the concept 'table'. The extension of the set is the tables, and the intension is the meaning 'table'. It has been recognized in modern philosophy and mathematics, as it was in medieval philosophy, that the intension cannot be reduced to the extension — see Ernst Cassirer, *Substance and Function* (New York, Dover, 1953), chapter 1.
61. The difference between unity in multiplicity and multiplicity in unity can be approached in a more mathematical manner. Clearly, One is not a number in the quantitative sense because it includes many, whereas one is such a number and therefore it must exclude many. The arithmetic of quantity is the arithmetic of one. It is the calculus of the extensive dimension of unity in multiplicity. Is there an arithmetic of One, which would therefore be the calculus of the intensive dimension of multiplicity in unity? At first sight it seems that this question is based on a contradiction. We identify arithmetic with the quantitative calculus of numbers. This is what we *mean* by arithmetic. So it would appear that it is impossible to have a non-numerical arithmetic. Nevertheless, such an arithmetic was discovered by Spencer Brown in the nineteen sixties, in the context of an investigation into the design of switching circuits in electronic engineering. It has been described in his book *Laws of Form* (London: Allen and Unwin, 1969), where he provides an interpretation of the basic operation in this arithmetic in

terms of the act of making a distinction. Thus, the non-numerical arithmetic which Spencer Brown discovered is seen by him as the calculus of distinction, analogously to the way that ordinary arithmetic is the calculus of number. It calculates with the form of distinction instead of with the form of quantity. Since the act of distinguishing is prior to counting, the calculus of distinction is a pre-numerical arithmetic.

The kind of distinction which Spencer Brown considers is the *extensive* distinction whereby one region is distinguished from another, one object from another, and so on. It has been shown by the writer that Spencer Brown's non-numerical arithmetic can also be interpreted as the calculus of the *intensive* distinction of multiplicity in unity. See P.H. Bortoft, op. cit. note 31, chapter 5. Thus it becomes the non-numerical arithmetic of the intensive dimension of One. It is therefore the arithmetic of wholeness. It can also be seen as the arithmetic of the *quality* of One instead of the quantity of one.

There are two primitive "equations" of this arithmetic:

$$\neg\,\neg \;=\; \neg \qquad\qquad\qquad \neg\,\neg \;=$$

The right-hand side of the second equation is blank intentionally — zero is counted as a number in mathematics, and therefore cannot appear as an element in a non-numerical arithmetic. When it is interpreted in terms of the intensive form of distinction, the first equation is the arithmetic of the whole which can be divided and yet remain whole. Thus, for example, when a hologram is divided there are two pieces of film numerically, but One hologram non-numerically. So the arithmetic of hologram division is:

$$\neg\,\neg \;=\; \neg$$

This is also the arithmetic of plant division when plants are propagated by vegetative reproduction. For example, if a fuchsia plant is divided into many pieces they will all grow until they flower, unless they are impaired by other circumstances. But each of these new plants are "parts" of the first plant. They are really one plant which has been divided and divided, and yet which remains whole even when the "parts" have become independent. The plant is One and many at the same time — like the fragments of a hologram. We do not recognize the One plant in this case because it is in the form of many. The analytical mode of consciousness is tuned towards seeing many ones, and not to seeing One in the form of many. It requires a transformation of consciousness to the holistic mode to be able to see the One that *is* the many — we could say that it is "hidden" in the many, hidden by our customary mode of consciousness. Similarly, this equation is also the arithmetic of the growth of the individual plant — because vegetative reproduction is only a special case of growth, i.e. growth accompanied by separation. This enables us to see the growing plant organically as a hologram in time, with the whole emerging within the whole instead of unit adding to unit as if the plant were like a pile of bricks or the accretion of a crystal. By actively looking at plants, plunging into the plant visually, followed by exact sensorial imagination, it is possible to learn to see the plant world in this way. This develops an organ of perception which is tuned towards the organic, and does not represent it conceptually in terms of the logic of solid bodies. Goethe said that "every process in nature, rightly observed, wakens in us a new organ of perception".

The second equation is the arithmetic of the relationship between the whole and the part. This relation can be expressed approximately by saying that the whole is "within" the part. This can be seen in the hologram, as well as in the relation between the archetypal organ and the organs of the plant, and between the archetypal plant and the different members of the plant kingdom. But the whole cannot be within the part extensively, because then either there would only be a single part, or else the whole would be divided into pieces. This also means that the relationship between whole and parts cannot be numerical. The whole is within the part intensively. There is an intensive distinction between the whole and the part, but without any extensive difference between them. The non-numerical arithmetic of this distinction is:

where the blank space represents the fact that there is no difference between the whole and the part in the intensive dimension of One. This relationship between the whole and the part is inside-out to how it appears in the extensive perspective — where we would say that the part is within the whole. The phenomenon of vegetative reproduction from cuttings can also be seen in the light of this intensive relationship between whole and part. Goethe recognized that not only does this show that the plant can be divided and yet remain whole, but also that the whole plant is potentially present in each part of its organism. He was particularly impressed when he saw a proliferated rose, i.e. a rose from the centre of which an entirely new plant had grown in place of the seed pod and organs of fertilization. He recognized in this phenomenon a vivid expression of the way that in the organic world the whole is within the part.

These two equations of the non-numerical arithmetic of wholeness are really two different aspects of the same thing, and they can therefore be combined. Thus, the non-numerical arithmetic of the process of dividing a hologram, or growing a plant from a cutting of itself, is given by combining:

$$\daleth = \qquad \text{and} \qquad \daleth\daleth = \daleth$$

to give

$$\daleth\daleth\daleth =$$

This is the arithmetic of the process in the intensive dimension of One, instead of in the extensive dimension of many ones. In this pre-numerical dimension the whole is within each part because the whole can be divided and yet remain whole.

It helps if these equations are themselves looked at in an intensive perspective, as if there is only one ⌐ in each equation because each ⌐ is the very same ⌐. This is a suggestive notation which can function as a symbolism, i.e. as a mirror in which the idea can be seen — although the 'idea' here is not an image but a *way* of seeing. Although Spencer Brown gives a name to the sign ⌐, there is no need to do so and it can be approached in a purely visual way. Such an approach in itself helps to·stimulate the transition to a holistic mode of consciousness. It is interesting that sometimes people become uneasy and annoyed if asked to do this. They demand to be told what it is called, so that they can read it verbally, and they show signs of relief if they are told. Since the analytical mode of consciousness is associated strongly with verbal behaviour, this could be an indication that the analytical mode is being inhibited by this simple device.

62. Plato called a Form "one over many", and maintained that such a Form was more real than the many particulars in which it is reflected. It has often been supposed that Plato made the mistake of hypostatizing a mental abstraction, and then separating it from the things from which it had been abstracted. For example, according to this view, the Form which is Beauty is the result of abstracting what is common to many particular instances of beauty, and then imagining that Beauty itself is somehow supposed to exist apart from these instances. In other words, it seems as if Plato had made the mistake of duplicating the world unnecessarily — the resulting dualism is often called the two-world theory. However, careful reading of Plato soon makes it clear that this confusion exists in the minds of those who attribute it to Plato, and not in Plato himself. Nevertheless, there does remain the problem of how the Forms are to be understood. In various places Plato brings out many of the difficulties himself. It may be that in so doing his aim was to show that the Forms cannot be understood by means of a way of thinking which is ultimately based on our experience in the world of bodies, i.e. on the logic of solid bodies. In other words, there is an ironic intention in Plato's "self-criticism". The major difficulty is with understanding how something can be simultaneously one and many. It is this difficulty which arises through imagining the Form in an extensive perspective, and which disappears in the perspective of multiplicity in unity and the intensive dimension of One. Similarly, it is the extensive perspective which is the source of the two-world theory which separates the Form from the particulars, and appears simply to duplicate the familiar world. It seems evident that Plato cannot be understood by verbal reasoning alone, because of the analytical mode of consioucness which is associated with the discursive intellectual mind.

63. See Owen Barfield, *Saving the Appearance* (New York: Harcourt, Brace and World, 1965), for an investigation into the attitude of empiricism as a form of idolatory.

64. Ernst Lehrs, op. cit., p.125. Also H.B. Nisbet, *Goethe and the Scientific Tradition* (University of London: Institute of Germanic Studies, 1972), p. 39.

65. In an essay, written towards the end of his life, Goethe said that he had

achieved in practice the power of intuitive reason which Kant had declared to be beyond the scope of the human mind. Kant believed that, although intuitive knowledge was possible in principle, it was not possible in practice for man, who was restricted to the power of discursive intellectual reason. See Ernst Lehrs, op. cit., pp. 73-76.

66. Erich Heller, *The Disinherited Mind* (Harmondsworth: Penguin Books, 1961), p. 12.

67. Agnes Arber, op. cit., p. 209.

68. See note 40.

69. Rudolf Steiner, *Riddles of Philosophy*, (New York: Anthroposophic Press, 1973), p. 183.

70. See section 2.2.1. above; also Harold I. Brown, op. cit., chapter 6.

71. Wolfgang Schad, *Man and Mammals: Toward a Biology of Form* (New York: Waldorf Press, 1977).

72. Schad's book abounds with such diagrams, which help to make it readable without getting lost in all the details that have to be taken into account.

73. Ibid., chapter 11.

74. Ibid., p. 30.

75. Hans-Georg Gadamer, *Truth and Method*, p. 432. The recognition that the objects of cognitive perception are meanings and not sense data, shows us that 'the world' is not an object, or set of objects, but a text. Cognitive perception is not simply sense perception, in which material objects are encountered through "the windows of the senses." It is literally, and not metaphorically, reading the text of the world. Harold Brown (op. cit. p. 88) compares the perception of meaning in observation with the more familiar case of the perception of meaning in reading a text. In the cognitive perception of, say, the objects in the room, the aspect of these objects which we encounter through the senses is equivalent to the material script of a text without the meaning. For sense perception alone, the material objects would be just like the meaningless squiggles of a script which we had not learned to read. Cognitive perception is the equivalent of reading the text directly, in which there is the immediate perception of meaning without noticing the script itself.

The reader can use his or her own experience of reading to explore this. It is also a useful exercise to read a text in English and then to look immediately at a text written in a script with which one is unfamiliar — say Arabic or Chinese. This makes the point quite clearly. The non-familiar script is an approximation to what our experience of the world would be like without the perception of meaning — what we recognize as the various objects in the world would be just like the elements of this script. The error of empiricism is now particularly clear : what it takes to be material objects are really a text, and what it believes to be sense perception is really an experience of reading.

This discovery that the world we perceive is not an object, but a text which we read, can be applied to scientific cognition in a way which makes the hermeneutic nature of Goethe's way of science particularly clear. Scientific cognition is one level up from everyday perception, in the sense that the individual meaning-objects at the everyday level now become like a script which we cannot read.

Thus, in the case of the mammals, we recognize individual mammal-types, and thus perceive meaning on this level, but we do not at first appearance perceive the overall organization of the different mammals. This organization, which is revealed through the discovery of relationships of form, is the perception of meaning at the level of scientific cognition. The relationships of form which Schad discovers are the language for which the observed mammals are the script. Before these relationships are perceived, we are in the position of a person who is in front of a script which is totally unfamiliar. The temptation is to side-step the contemplation of the phenomena at this point, and instead rely on the verbal-intellectual mind. The result of doing so is that we read meanings *into* the phenomena by our own intellectual activity, instead of learning to read the phenomena directly. The phenomenologist of nature really is the *hermeneutic* phenomenologist, and Goethe's way of science is therefore quite properly described as the hermeneutics of nature. Goethe meant it literally when he said that nature is a text which he was learning to read.

76. This is precisely what happened to David Hume in his attempt to understand the relationship of causality. Hume's philosophy will be discussed further below.

77. Schad, op. cit., p. 118.

78. Ibid., p. 11. If "life exists only as a continuing present", it clearly cannot be described in the framework of analytical time, i.e. the sequential instantaneous snapshot idea of time which belongs to the analytical mode of consciousness. The kind of temporality which is characteristic of life itself, i.e. a continuing present, is hinted at in the perception of change and motion in the holistic mode of consciousness. Compare also Goethe's comment on causality (note 33) with the assertion here that "in life, causes and effects take place simultaneously and complement one another".

79. Ibid., p. 153.

80. Charles Darwin, *The Origin of Species* (Harmondsworth: Penguin Books, 1968).

81. David Hume, *A Treatise on Human Nature, Book One* (Glasgow: Fontana/Collins, 1962).

82. Ibid., p. 331.

83. Cf. the story of Mulla Nasrudin and the donkeys, which encapsulates the problem here succintly, in Idries Shah, *The Sufis* (New York: Doubleday, 1964), p. 59.

84. Roger Bacon distinguished these two ways in the thirteenth century. Idries Shah points out that the way of experience became interpreted narrowly in the sense of experiment, and this "has prevented the scientific researcher from approaching knowledge by means of itself". (See *The Sufis*, op. cit. p. xxvi.)

85. Aristotle is usually thought of as an arch-rationalist who proceeded by deductive reasoning from first principles. In fact he was a master observer of nature. He was an experientialist but not an empiricist, because he did not limit experience to the senses. On the other hand, he was also not an analytical rationalist who limited the mind to logical thought and denied it the possibility of experience through perceptive insight. His scientific work involved detailed sensory observation, and insight into what is not visible to the senses as such by

what he called intuitive induction. It has now been suggested that the ideal of deductive reasoning, with which Aristotle has been identified, may have been meant to apply to the way in which scientific knowledge should be presented and taught, and not to how such knowledge is discovered in the first place. See Barnes, Schofield and Sarabji (eds.), *Articles on Aristotle, Vol. 1: Science* (London: Duckworth, 1975), p. 77. Because Goethe worked by observation and intuition, it may well be that his way of science can provide the kind of *experience* which is needed to understand this philosopher, who has usually been interpreted exclusively in terms of the analytical mode of consciousness which is associated with the logical mind.

86. Saul Kripke, *Naming and Necessity* (Oxford: Blackwell, 1980). See also John Cottingham, *Rationalism* (London: Granada, 1984), pp. 115-120, for a simplified account. Since the time of Leibniz, philosophers have distinguished between 'truths of reason' and 'truths of fact'. The former are necessarily true because they do not depend on anything outside their own meaning. For example, it is impossible for the proposition 'all triangles are three-sided' to be wrong, and we can know this with certainty without ever needing to refer to anything beyond our own minds. But this kind of proposition does not tell us anything about the world. The proposition 'it is raining', on the other hand, does tell us something about the world. But such a proposition can be false, and therefore, if true, it is only contingently true and not true of necessity. This division became a dogma of modern empiricism. Kripke's suggestion, that there can be propositions which are about the world and yet necessarily true, needs to be seen against this background to be appreciated. This is not the only way in which the traditional division into truths of reason and truths of fact has been called into question. For reasons which are different to Kripke's, the contemporary philosophy of science also rejects this dogma — see Harold I. Brown, op. cit., chapter 7, especially p. 105.

87. See G. Webster and B.C. Goodwin, "The Origin of Species: a Structuralist Approach", *J. Social. Biol. Struct.* vol. 5, 1982, p. 29.

88. Charles Darwin, op. cit., p. 90.

89. G. Webster and B.C. Goodwin, op. cit., p. 16.

90. Ernst Cassirer, *The Problem of Knowledge*, p. 167.

91. G. Webster and B.C. Goodwin, op. cit., p. 42.

92. Descartes, *Discourse on Method and the Meditations* (Hardmondsworth: Penguin Books, 1968).

93. Ibid., p. 107, for example. In letters to various correspondents, Descartes showed just how widely he intended 'thinking' and 'thought' to be taken. Although at the beginning of the *Meditations* he is clearly concerned with the *act* of thinking, he soon includes many other functions under the heading of thought, such as sight and hearing, which we would not usually describe in this way. Even a toothache becomes a thought for Descartes, from which it is evident that he eventually came to mean by 'thought' nothing more than subjective experience.

94. See Antony Flew, *An Introduction to Western Philosophy* (London: Thames and Hudson, 1971), p. 300.

95. See Hans-Georg Gadamer, *Philosophical Hermeneutics*, op. cit., p. 119.

96. See Roger Scruton, *A Short History of Modern Philosophy* (London: Routledge and Kegan Paul, 1984), p. 132. Hume was not able to recognize the significance of his achievement at the time, consequently he was only able to experience it in its negative aspect.

97. Owen Barfield, *Romanticism Comes of Age* (London: Rudolf Steiner Press, 1966), p. 36.

98. According to Aquinas, the *species intelligibilis* is the mode of being of the perceived object in the observer, so that when this is created by the *intellectus agens* the object is, in a sense, within us and we are the object. See E.J. Dijksterhuis, *The Mechanization of the World Picture* (Oxford: Oxford University Press, 1969), p. 148; also Owen Barfield, *Saving the Appearances*, chapter 13.

99. Hans-Georg Gadamer, *Truth and Method*, p. 416.

100. Rudolf Steiner, *Goethe the Scientist*, p. 179. Now we can reverse the direction of influence here, and use Goethe's way of science to provide the *experience* which is needed to understand the philosophy of Schelling.

101. Historians of science now recognize that *Naturphilosophie* influenced the development of mainstream physics in a number of ways. For example, the idea of a single unifying force for all natural phenomena, which has influenced physics in a profound way, came from *Naturphilosophie* initially. The discovery of the conservation of energy in thermodynamics, and the discovery of electromagnetism, were both influenced directly by this philosophical guiding idea. See Thomas S. Kuhn, "Energy Conservation as an Example of Simultaneous Discovery," in *The Essential Tension* (Chicago: University of Chicago Press, 1977), pp. 97-100. Also, L. Pearce Williams, *The Origins of Field Theory* (New York: Random House, 1966). The influence of *Naturphilosophie* on the growth of biology (in the areas of embryology, evolution, and the cell theory) is described in Stephen F. Mason, *A History of Science* (New York: Collier Books, 1962). The role of such a priori guiding ideas in scientific discovery is discussed widely in the literature of the history and philosophy of science. See particularly Kurt Hübner, *Critique of Scientific Reason* (Chicago: University of Chicago Press, 1983).

102. *Nature*, Vol. 1 no. 1, November 4, 1869, p. 10.

103. See Jeremy Naydler, "The Regeneration of Realism and the Recovery of a Science of Qualities", *International Philosophical Quarterly*, Vol.XXIII, 1983, pp.155-172.